divorce &
remarriage

a permanence view

Daryl Wingerd

Jim Elliff

Jim Chrisman

Steve Burchett

ISBN 978-0-9820968-0-2

Additional copies of *Divorce and Remarriage: A Permanence View* and other
publications may be ordered online at www.CCWtoday.org.

Published by *Christian Communicators Worldwide*
Kansas City (Parkville), Missouri, USA.

Cover design by Tony Barmann

CHRISTIAN COMMUNICATORS *Worldwide*
www.CCWtoday.org

Table of Contents

Table of Contents (continued)

Preface

Divorce and wrongful remarriage are forgivable sins. We want to start here, at the heart of our faith in Christ. When Jesus died, He did not fail to atone for the misdeeds of His people in this critical area. Even the person who has acted as wrongly as possible in this matter may be fully forgiven, and may have a fulfilled life of service to God after repentance. Also, God mercifully blesses many second marriages that began sinfully. This is a mystery for which we can all be extremely grateful.

Most conservative Christian leaders take the view that divorce and remarriage are permissible when one spouse has committed adultery. Others add desertion by a disobedient spouse as an exception to Jesus' prohibition of remarriage after divorce. Still others go beyond that in terms of permissiveness, but this is not usually the case within more conservative evangelical churches. In this book we are moving the marker over to what we have come to believe is God's original intent and ongoing expectation for marriage. We are contending for a no-divorce, no-remarriage position, with no exceptions for adultery or desertion. We call our position "the permanence view."

Our view arose out of two years of study as a team of elders and interns of a new church. We knew that we did not have the luxury of having *no* opinion on this important aspect of church life, and we wished to have our view clearly in mind prior to any need for it. As elders we wanted to be prepared for whatever situation might occur, and to be able to instruct others according to what we believe to be the will of God.

Each of us came into this period of study with a view that allowed for divorce on the basis of adultery. Our former views, when consistently taught and practiced, were certainly conservative when compared with those of society as a whole, as well as those of more liberal churches. (Religious groups that advocate same-sex unions are hardly concerned about the issues we are dealing with here.) Our current view calls for a significant change in action on the part of the local church. According to our former position, divorce and remarriage are tolerated in cases of the destructive behavior of unrepentant adulterous spouses. According to our current view, the same cases call for counsel against divorce and remarriage, and even church discipline if a church member disregards this counsel.

At first we dismissed what has now become our view. For months, in fact, we worked against it. Yet, as time went on, we came to embrace this position as the only way to harmonize the Scriptures. Further study with the men of our church brought us even more assurance as they probed us and helped us think through every detail. These men are well-studied, serious-minded believers. Next, we met twice with a group of pastors in our area. These were amiable and helpful meetings through which we gained valuable insight. Finally, we asked a number of pastors, professors, and Christian leaders from around the country to review our manuscript. They did not all concur with our conclusions, but their ruminations, questions, and challenges helped us to both confirm and improve our position so that we could present it in its most lucid form. We thank them for their kindness in the search for truth in this vital area of pastoral theology.

From the outset, we ask your patience with us. As soon as our permanence view is perceived as permitting *no* divorce, and *no* remarriage after divorce (unless former spouses have died), many will begin thinking, "What about this situation? What about that person? Where does this view leave *me*?" and so on. We have addressed questions related to these practical matters in the second part of the book. The first part is dedicated to the straightforward laying out of the biblical teaching. We ask, therefore, that you read the first part carefully before reading our counsel for practical application. What we *do* as Christians must be grounded on what we *believe* Christ commands or forbids. Until we are certain that we know His will for divorce and remarriage as the result of studying the applicable texts of Scripture, we cannot be certain that we are acting in a manner that pleases Him.

Some of the pastoral implications of our view may surprise you. For instance, we do not believe that divorce or wrongful remarriage automatically prohibits a man who has repented of these sins from becoming an elder or deacon in a church. We also do not promote the policy that every person in a church where the permanence position is adopted must necessarily concur with this position (though they must acknowledge that it will be taught and practiced). Additionally, we do not believe that a person in a wrongful second marriage is committing adultery through each intimate act with his or her spouse. Lastly, we believe and teach that marriages that began sinfully are true marriages, that they can be healthy and happy, and that they should be nourished and cherished in a manner that honors Christ.

One of the most sobering realities coming out of our study is that even those conservative churches and leaders who hold less restrictive views are not immune to the difficulties related to divorce and remarriage. If the leaders of a local church draw a line *anywhere* on the continuum of permissiveness, action must be taken when that line is crossed by one of their members. Consider, for example, a local church where the agreed-upon position is that divorce and remarriage are permitted by God, but only in cases of adultery. What will be done in terms of church discipline when a member initiates a divorce for some other reason? What if a marriage involving a divorced member is being planned, but the member's former divorce would not have been permitted according to the church's current position? The leaders of such a church must act decisively and correctively in situations like these if they are to be consistent with their own convictions. Questions concerning church polity must also be faced. For example, will church membership be granted to those who formerly divorced and/or remarried for reasons other than adultery, yet who remain unrepentant because they believe their actions were allowed by God? Our no-divorce, no-remarriage position may lead to more struggles, but less restrictive churches and leaders will experience the same difficulties in the remaining cases. Whatever our view, we all have much to think about.

We also recognize the high stakes involved in stating an opinion such as ours. If our view is wrong, and if some are persuaded to act according to our conclusions, we will have prevented some marriages and divorces from taking place that should have been permitted. We would be grieved to discover that we were responsible for such an error and its consequences. But if more permissive views are in error, believers who promote and defend them are allowing a violation of Christ's command, "What therefore God has joined together, let no man separate" (Matt. 19:6; Mark 10:9), and are condoning an act of adultery by permitting remarriage after divorce.

You must come to your own conclusions. We are not presuming to dictate what you must believe or do. You will stand before God on this issue just as we will. We simply believe we are being obedient to Christ to lay out the results of our study for others to consider. We also recognize the complexity of the issue and believe that godly people can disagree. Therefore, differences between Bible believing churches on this issue must not be permitted to affect our fellowship with each other, since we all concur that the Word of God is our infallible final authority. Additionally, we ask this indulgence: If you find error in one part of our work because of our incompetence or blindness, please do not let this prevent you from considering the whole argument. We might be wrong on one part, but right on the main premise.

If we, by the grace of God, have arrived at a position that is closer to the mind of God, then we will be gratified to know that God has used us to help others whom we love dearly. We trust that we will in no way hinder what is permitted or give license for what is prohibited. We want God to be glorified and marriages to be saved.

Daryl Wingerd, Jim Elliff, Jim Chrisman, and Steve Burchett
Elders, Christ Fellowship of Kansas City
www.ChristFellowshipKC.org

This book was originally a lengthy position paper on the subject of divorce and remarriage. Since it still bears some of the characteristics of a position paper, it may be adopted in general as support for a church's shorter policy statement. We have provided a brief statement churches may use or modify for adopting the permanence view (see appendix 3).

We hope to engage in a continuing dialogue on this subject. If you have further questions about what is written, please contact us through the website of *Christian Communicators Worldwide* at www.CCWtoday.org. Some of these questions may be added anonymously to an online dialogue page along with our responses.

Part 1

Examining the Biblical Texts

Introduction to Part 1

Divorce and remarriage are painful subjects to address biblically in our culture for at least three reasons. First, the practice of divorce has reached epidemic proportions even among those who profess to be Christians. Nearly every Christian knows someone in his or her local church who has been divorced. Second, most Christians who divorce also remarry, usually with the strong encouragement of other Christians but often without a thorough, personal understanding of what the Bible has to say about second marriages. Third, not everyone agrees as to what *is* the biblical position regarding divorce and remarriage. As a result, Christians in potential divorce and/or remarriage situations often receive conflicting counsel from different, though equally qualified and respected, pastors and teachers.

Our understanding of the Bible's teaching on marriage, divorce, and remarriage may be summarized in three main assertions:

1. The one-flesh union created in marriage[1] is permanent until death.

In the Bible, the remarriage of a divorced person is consistently said to be an act of adultery, indicating that the one-flesh union created by God when a marriage begins is not ended by divorce. Only death dissolves this union.

---

1 We will not try to define marriage customs and laws in exhaustive detail, but whenever and wherever a marriage exists, it is essentially a relationship between a man and a woman involving 1) a voluntary commitment of each to the other (i.e., a covenant commitment, whether stated or unstated), 2) recognition by the surrounding culture that the two have become husband and wife, and 3) sexual union. The true definition of marriage never includes homosexual unions.

2. Initiating a divorce is never lawful.[2]
The defining principle in Jesus' teaching on divorce and
remarriage is that initiating a divorce is always unlawful, and
there are no compelling reasons to see His prohibition of
divorce as less than absolute.

**3. Remarrying after divorce is an act of adultery if a former
spouse is living.**
Because the one-flesh union remains intact even when
the external arrangement called marriage is terminated by
divorce, remarriage after divorce while a former spouse is
living constitutes a violation of the permanent one-flesh union.

In Part 1, we will explain and defend these three assertions by
examining the pertinent biblical texts. In Part 2, we will apply our
conclusions to believers and churches.

---

2 Believers may cooperate in divorce proceedings when an unbelieving spouse insists on ending
the marriage (1 Cor. 7:15), but they are never permitted to initiate a divorce themselves, or to
encourage or pressure an unbelieving spouse to initiate a divorce.

1

Some Uncomplicated Words of Jesus

Jesus' words are not always easy to understand. We know He was not confused when He spoke, and we are certain that out of all He said, the Spirit included everything in the Bible that is essential. Yet, the peculiarities of the ancient culture Jesus addressed, along with our limited ability to access the background information (not to mention the hindrance of our sometimes sluggish minds), often make what should be perfectly lucid seem nearly impossible to comprehend.

We are aware that Jesus said more about divorce and remarriage than we are going to look at in this first chapter. We know, for instance, that He included an "exception clause," as recorded in two places in Matthew's Gospel. We will examine that controversial clause later, but first we want to take a brief look at some of His *un*complicated words.

On the subject of divorce, both Matthew and Mark record the following statement:

> What therefore God has joined together, let no man separate. (Matt. 19:6; Mark 10:9)

This was Jesus' initial response to the Pharisees when they asked Him whether or not it was lawful for a man to divorce his wife. Not everyone agrees as to the precise intent of the Pharisees' question (as we will explain later), but whatever their intent, Jesus' straightforward answer seems to transcend any controversy. His simple response, based on the first words in the Bible about marriage (Gen. 2:24), reveals two facts about marriage and divorce:

- When a man and woman marry, God joins them together.

- No person is permitted to separate what God has joined together.

The comprehensiveness of this statement leaves no room for equivocation. Once joined together by God, the marriage is to be permanent.

Jesus also uttered some uncomplicated words about remarriage after divorce. Here is the first passage:

> Whoever divorces his wife and marries another woman commits adultery against her; and if she herself divorces her husband and marries another man, she is committing adultery. (Mark 10:11-12)

Again, two important truths are revealed:

- Whenever a man divorces his wife and marries another woman, he commits adultery.

- Whenever a woman divorces her husband and marries another man, she commits adultery.

Jesus made this statement to His disciples when He was alone with them in a house. It followed a longer discussion on the subject with a group of Pharisees (vv. 2-9). The simple words of verses 11 and 12 are the ones the Spirit of God chose to place in Mark's Gospel as a summary of Jesus' encounter with the Pharisees.

Jesus' words about remarriage after divorce are also found in Luke's Gospel. The Spirit of God moved Luke to record this single and concise statement:

> Everyone who divorces his wife and marries another commits adultery, and he who marries one who is divorced from a husband commits adultery. (Luke 16:18)

Once again Jesus' words are unambiguous, revealing the following facts:

- Every person who divorces a spouse and marries someone else commits adultery.

- Every person who marries a divorced person commits adultery.

In the next three chapters, we will offer explanations of three main conclusions that have arisen from our study of divorce and remarriage. We are hopeful that we are clear and uncomplicated all the way through our discussion, but even if we are not, please remember the plain words of Christ recorded by Matthew, Mark, and Luke. There is much to consider in the Bible on the subject of divorce and remarriage, but there is also a sense in which the teaching of Scripture is amazingly simple. In fact, the interpreter's task is to look hard at the apparent difficulties of a subject until the complexities meld together with the plain statements, resulting in the most unified and comprehensible (even if challenging) meaning.

You may not agree that the above statements from Jesus are "plain" or "simple." Perhaps you cannot read them without thinking of other places where the teaching of the New Testament is admittedly more complex. We respect those who differ with us, but we have examined these three statements from every imaginable angle and remain convinced that they must be dealt with, first and foremost, on the basis of their immediately accessible meanings. Grammatically and linguistically, they are not at all difficult to comprehend. Some readers may believe we have oversimplified the complex, but we would caution against the tendency to overcomplicate the simple.

Regardless of what you conclude after reading this book, you must contend with *all* that Jesus said about divorce and remarriage. The three passages mentioned above will never be erased, nullified, or rendered less important to the overall discussion because other passages receive the most scrutiny. We will mention them repeatedly and work through them carefully because we do not want them to be neglected. These passages should be viewed as towers on the landscape of our discussion. We will do well to glance up at them often.

Before we look at our three main assertions about the Bible's teaching on divorce and remarriage more closely, let us state them once again:

- The one-flesh union created in marriage is permanent until death.

- Initiating a divorce is never lawful.

- Remarrying after divorce is an act of adultery if a former spouse is living.

2

First Assertion: The One-flesh Union Created in Marriage is Permanent Until Death

When a group of Pharisees came to Jesus to test Him, asking whether or not it was lawful for a man to divorce his wife,[3] (Matt. 19:3, Mark 10:2), Jesus responded like this:

> Have you not read that He who created them from the beginning made them male and female, and said, "For this reason a man shall leave his father and mother and be joined to his wife, and the two shall become one flesh"? So they are no longer two, but one flesh. What therefore God has joined together, let no man separate. (Matt. 19:4-6; cf. Mark 10:6-9)

Jesus' answer to the Pharisees' question was an unqualified "No." His response reveals that when a marriage takes place, God providentially joins a man and a woman together in a morally binding union that is indissoluble. This permanent union is created in a consummated marriage no matter what types of attitudes and/ or circumstances brought the couple together as husband and wife. The man and woman who meet and marry quickly, for instance, but regret the hasty commitment in the days or weeks that follow, are nevertheless permanently bound to one another. Any marriage, however ill-advised or regrettable, was ordained by God and is permanently binding.

---

3 We are aware that Matthew included the words "for any reason at all" at the end of the Pharisees' question, while Mark paraphrased the question as we did in the opening paragraph of this chapter. For our discussion about the significance of this difference between Matthew and Mark, see the section entitled, "The Intent of the Question Itself: Seeking Harmony Between Matthew and Mark," in chapter 8.

Jesus referred to the nature and permanence of this union when He said, "So they are no longer two, but one flesh" (Matt. 19:6; Mark 10:8). The biblical language Jesus referred to (Gen. 2:24, "they shall become one flesh") assumes that the couple is passive in one sense, with God Himself joining them together at the deepest level.

Jesus affirmed this when He followed this statement in Matthew 19 and Mark 10 by saying, "What therefore *God* has joined together, let no man separate" (Matt. 19:6; Mark 10:9, emphasis added).[4]

Additionally, the New Testament teaches that no one other than God can dissolve the one-flesh union. Divorce does not end that which God has established as permanent. Despite civil laws and personal opinions to the contrary, only death, which God alone ordains, can dissolve the one-flesh union. We can be certain that this is true because, as Jesus said, remarriage after divorce is an act of adultery:

> Everyone who divorces his wife, except for the reason of unchastity, makes her commit adultery; and whoever marries a divorced woman commits adultery. (Matt. 5:32)

> Whoever divorces his wife and marries another woman commits adultery against her; and if she herself divorces her husband and marries another man, she is committing adultery. (Mark 10:11-12)

> Everyone who divorces his wife and marries another commits adultery, and he who marries one who is divorced from a husband commits adultery. (Luke 16:18)

The Apostle Paul clearly agreed, saying,

> For the married woman is bound by law to her husband while he is living; but if her husband dies, she is released from the law concerning the husband. So then, if while her husband

---

4 The one-flesh union (which is the terminology we will use often) should not be thought of as the joining of two distinct personal entities into one new personal entity. A man and woman who marry become "one" as a couple, but they remain distinct as persons who are individually accountable before God. When the Bible uses the term "one flesh" in a marriage context, it most likely refers to a combination of the following: 1) the new family unit God has created by bringing the man and woman together, 2) the covenant obligation between a husband and wife which was established and ratified by God at the time of their marriage, and 3) the sexual union by which the marriage was consummated.

is living she is joined to another man, she shall be called an adulteress; but if her husband dies, she is free from the law, so that she is not an adulteress though she is joined to another man. (Rom. 7:2-3)[5]

An act of sex between a man and a woman is called "adultery" only when it violates an existing one-flesh union. Because remarriage after divorce (while the original spouse is living) is called "adultery," it is evident that the one-flesh union with the former spouse still exists in some form. The union created by God in marriage is not *un*-created by the act of divorce. As D.A Carson comments on Matthew 5:32, "Anyone who divorces his wife is at fault, because he is causing her to commit adultery if she marries someone else, since the first link is not really broken."[6] Since divorce does not dissolve the one-flesh union, it naturally follows to say that the union is permanent until death (Rom. 7:3; 1 Cor. 7:39).

Jesus' prohibition of divorce in Matthew 19:6 and Mark 10:9 is sometimes thought to refute the above point. Since He commands us *not* to separate what God has joined together, it is reasoned that it is *possible* to separate what God has joined together. After all, why would He prohibit us from doing something that is impossible? But by looking at the matter in its fuller biblical context (as is the intent of this book), we will see that Jesus must have been prohibiting the external separation of marriage. The vows spoken at a wedding certainly can be disregarded, and a marriage certainly can be separated in civil and legal ways, but these external disruptions of marriage do not and cannot destroy the morally binding one-flesh union created by God. Otherwise, no reason would exist for Jesus to call remarriage after divorce "adultery."

---

5 Paul's purpose in Romans 7 was not to teach about divorce and remarriage. He was teaching Christians about their relationship to the Law. Nevertheless, his meaning concerning the Law would have only been understandable to his readers if his illustration about marriage was both familiar and true. Therefore, what he says about divorce and remarriage in this passage is applicable to our study.

6 D. A. Carson, *Jesus' Sermon on the Mount* (Toronto: Global Christian Publishers, 1999), 48. We will discuss the meaning of the exception clause in Matthew 5:32, "except for the reason of unchastity," in chapter 6.

3

Second Assertion: Initiating a Divorce is Never Lawful

Jesus prohibited initiating a divorce categorically, using absolute and universal terms. He said, "What therefore God has joined together, let no man separate" (Matt. 19:6; Mark 10:9). The point of the command is to say that no *man* (whether male or female) should attempt to destroy what *God* has created. In both Matthew 19 and Mark 10, this statement was Jesus' answer to the Pharisees' question about whether or not it was lawful for a man to divorce his wife. In response to this question, Jesus' answer was "No."

The Pharisees obviously recognized Jesus' response as a rejection of their permissive stance on divorce. This is why they asked in protest, "Why then did Moses command to give her a certificate of divorce and send her away?" (Matt. 19:7, cf. Deut. 24:1). Consider the passage to which the Pharisees appealed:

> When a man takes a wife and marries her, and it happens that she finds no favor in his eyes because he has found some indecency in her, and he writes her a certificate of divorce and puts it in her hand and sends her out from his house, and she leaves his house and goes and becomes another man's wife, and if the latter husband turns against her and writes her a certificate of divorce and puts it in her hand and sends her out of his house, or if the latter husband dies who took her to be his wife, then her former husband who sent her away is not allowed to take her again to be his wife, since she has been defiled; for that is an abomination before the Lord, and you

shall not bring sin on the land which the Lord your God gives you as an inheritance. (Deut. 24:1-4)

By the time of Christ, most Jews had come to understand Deuteronomy 24:1-4 as giving *active* permission to divorce (as if Moses were saying, "You *may* divorce your wives."). They had found a way, however illegitimate, to interpret Moses' words to their own personal advantage, making both divorce and remarriage allowable. But a careful reading of Deuteronomy 24:1-4 will show that the only legislation laid down by Moses is the prohibition of a wife returning to the first husband after 1) he has divorced her, 2) she has married another man, and 3) the second marriage has ended either by divorce or the death of the second husband. If all three of these things have happened, the first husband may not take her back as his wife. No *active* permission is given in this passage for a man to divorce his wife. The only "permission" related to divorce in Deuteronomy 24 is the *passive* permission implied by Moses *not* putting an end to this sinful practice.[7]

In response to the Pharisees' protest of His prohibition of divorce, Jesus answered their appeal to Deuteronomy 24 like this:

> Because of your hardness of heart Moses permitted you to divorce your wives [The KJV appropriately renders this, 'Moses . . . suffered you to put away your wives']; but from the beginning it has not been this way." (Matt. 19:8)

Jesus was revealing the Pharisees' interpretive error. He informed them that the legislation in Deuteronomy 24 did not reflect God's original intent for marriage but was only given as a concession to their sinful practice. He instructed them to look back further than Deuteronomy for their divorce legislation, pointing them instead to the very beginning of marriage in Genesis 2:24. And the legislation that stems from Genesis 2:24, as Jesus stated it, is this: "So they are no longer two, but one flesh. What therefore God has joined together, let no man separate" (Matt. 19:6; cf. Mark 10:8-9).

---

7 A few translations render verse 1 in ways that make it appear that Moses permitted divorce in the active sense. The KJV, for example, says, "then let him write her a bill of divorcement, and give it in her hand, and send her out of his house." Interestingly, the wording is changed in the NKJV to extend passive permission only, as we described above. This change represents the majority view among modern scholars and translators, as reflected in the ESV, NASB, NKJV, NIV, TNIV, NJB, NLT, RSV, NRSV, and NAB.

In Matthew 19:9, Jesus appears to give one exception to this rule—divorce because of fornication (Greek, *porneia*). The phrase in Matthew 19:9 that appears to provide an exception to Jesus' no-divorce rule ("except for immorality") is commonly referred to as the "exception clause." A similar "exception clause" is found in Matthew 5:32. These two critical verses, which we will address in detail later, read as follows:

> It was said, "Whoever sends his wife away, let him give her a certificate of divorce"; but I say to you that everyone who divorces his wife, **except for the reason of unchastity** [*porneia*], makes her commit adultery; and whoever marries a divorced woman commits adultery. (Matt. 5:31-32, emphasis added)

> And I say to you, whoever divorces his wife, **except for immorality** [*porneia*], and marries another woman commits adultery. (Matt. 19:9, emphasis added)

The question is this: Do the words "except for immorality" in Matthew 19:9 provide a true exception to Jesus' absolute prohibition of divorce in Matthew 19:6? Did He qualify the legislation He had just stated and defended? Or does the exception clause mean something else? From an interpretive standpoint, unless there are compelling exegetical reasons to take Jesus' prohibition of divorce as less than absolute, we must interpret Matthew 19:9 in a way that preserves the categorical nature of His original answer to the Pharisees' question. This is particularly critical when we realize that the same absolute prohibition of divorce—"What therefore God has joined together, let no man separate"—is given in Mark 10:9 with no hint of any exceptions.

Perhaps the most important factor in this discussion is the way in which Jesus' teaching on divorce was interpreted by the Apostle Paul. Paul paraphrased Jesus' basic teaching about divorce and remarriage in 1 Corinthians 7:10-11:

> But to the married I give instructions, not I, but the Lord, that the wife should not leave her husband (but if she does leave, she must remain unmarried, or else be reconciled to her husband), and that the husband should not divorce his wife.

As Paul insisted, these two verses are instructions from Jesus. There is no legitimate reason to conclude otherwise when Paul said, "But to the married I give instructions, *not I, but the Lord*" (v. 10, emphasis added). With this introduction, the parenthetical phrase in verse 11, "but if she does leave, she must remain unmarried, or else be reconciled to her husband," should not be seen as an addition to, or qualification of, what Jesus taught. It is an essential component of Jesus' instructions. Therefore, it seems almost impossible *not* to conclude that these two verses reflect Paul's understanding of Jesus' overall teaching on divorce and remarriage.

Jesus' consistent message regarding divorce and remarriage may be summarized in two statements: 1) Man is not to separate what God has joined together, and 2) Whoever divorces one person and marries another person commits adultery. If Matthew 19:9 provides an actual exception to these two principles, one would think Paul would reflect that exception in His paraphrase of Jesus' teaching. But he does not. Rather, Paul's prohibition of divorce in 1 Corinthians 7 is in perfect and obvious agreement with the no-divorce, no-remarriage teaching of Christ. When the question of divorce is addressed, Paul responds as follows:

The wife should not leave her husband. (v. 10)

The husband should not divorce his wife. (v. 11)

If any brother has a wife who is an unbeliever, and she consents to live with him, he must not divorce her. (v. 12)

A woman who has an unbelieving husband, and he consents to live with her, she must not send her husband away. (v. 13)

Four times in this chapter Paul says, in effect, "Do not divorce your spouse." The closest he ever comes to an exception to this rule is in verse 15 where the believing spouse is permitted to *cooperate* in a divorce if the unbelieving spouse insists on leaving. Paul gives no support for the idea that in certain cases it is lawful to *initiate* a divorce. He even prohibits divorcing an unbelieving spouse. When we call to mind the rampant immorality in Corinth (cf. 1 Cor. 6:9-20), we should realize that being married to an unbeliever sometimes meant being married to an adulterer or adulteress. There is no reason to appeal to Paul to justify a permissive stance on divorce.

4

Third Assertion: Remarrying After Divorce is an Act of Adultery if a Former Spouse is Living

As we said in chapter 2, the one-flesh union created by God in marriage is permanent. Though marriages can be, and frequently are, severed externally in civil and legal ways, the one-flesh union can only be separated by God Himself through death. This is why marriage to any other person after divorce, as long as a former spouse is living, is consistently called "adultery." Not including Matthew 19:9 with its exception clause, Jesus made this clear in the following statements:

> Whoever marries a divorced woman commits adultery. (Matt. 5:32)

> Whoever divorces his wife and marries another woman commits adultery against her; and if she herself divorces her husband and marries another man, she is committing adultery. (Mark 10:11-12)

> Everyone who divorces his wife and marries another commits adultery, and he who marries one who is divorced from a husband commits adultery. (Luke 16:18)

These verses clearly provide no exceptions to the rule that remarriage after divorce is an act of adultery. The second part of Luke 16:18 even seems to disallow the wife's remarriage in the event that her husband has divorced her *and has already married someone else* (as described in the first part of the verse). Furthermore, Paul does not soften Jesus' stance against divorce or remarriage. Consider the following comparison:

Jesus disallows divorce without exception:

> What therefore God has joined together, let no man separate. (Matt. 19:6; Mark 10:9)

Paul does the same:

> The wife should not leave her husband . . . the husband should not divorce his wife. (1 Cor. 7:10, 11b; cf. vv. 12-13).

Understanding that divorce may still occur, Jesus prohibits remarriage after divorce:

> Whoever marries a divorced woman commits adultery. (Matt. 5:32b)

> Whoever divorces his wife and marries another woman commits adultery against her; and if she herself divorces her husband and marries another man, she is committing adultery. (Mark 10:11-12)

> Everyone who divorces his wife and marries another commits adultery, and he who marries one who is divorced from a husband commits adultery. (Luke 16:18)

Paul, also understanding that divorce may occur, does the same:

> But if she does leave, she must remain unmarried, or else be reconciled to her husband. (1 Cor. 7:11)

Paul's representation of Christ's overall teaching regarding divorce and remarriage is a perfect summary of what we have in the Gospels. Both Jesus and Paul disallow divorce, and both disallow remarriage after divorce. The only difference is that Jesus prohibits remarriage after divorce *by* calling it "adultery," while Paul prohibits remarriage after divorce *without* calling it "adultery."

Paul's prohibition of remarriage after divorce is further affirmed at the end of 1 Corinthians 7 where he finally gives one exception to the no-remarriage rule:

> A wife is bound as long as her husband lives; but if her husband is dead, she is free to be married to whom she wishes, only in the Lord. (v. 39)

By only mentioning this one exception, in concluding his teaching about marriage, divorce, and remarriage, Paul affirms that this is the *only* situation that justifies remarriage. He says the same thing in Romans 7:

> For the married woman is bound by law to her husband while he is living; but if her husband dies, she is released from the law concerning the husband. So then, if while her husband is living she is joined to another man, she shall be called an adulteress; but if her husband dies, she is free from the law, so that she is not an adulteress though she is joined to another man. (vv. 2-3).

Despite these factors, many Christians believe that Matthew 19:9 provides an actual exception to Jesus' no-divorce, no-remarriage teaching. Additionally, three verses in 1 Corinthians 7 (vv. 9, 15, and 28) are often taken to mean that in some cases Paul permitted remarriage after divorce even if a former spouse was still living. We will address Matthew 19:9 and the three verses from 1 Corinthians 7 in subsequent chapters. In our view these texts do not provide an exception to Jesus' no-divorce, no-remarriage rule.

5

The Question of Interpretive Priority

The exception clause in Matthew 19:9 (cf. Matt. 5:32) is the primary wording appealed to by those who say that both divorce and remarriage should be permitted in cases of marital unfaithfulness. Consider the verse once again:

> And I say to you, whoever divorces his wife, except for immorality, and marries another woman commits adultery.

We understand how Matthew 19:9 leads many Christians to conclude that both divorce and remarriage are permitted in the case of adultery. They interpret the exception clause in a way that seems to be the obvious reading, allowing for both divorce and remarriage in cases of *porneia* (i.e., "immorality," which they understand to mean "adultery" in this context). They then use this interpretation of Matthew 19:9 as the key to understanding the Bible's overall teaching on divorce and remarriage. Texts that contain no exceptions are then interpreted as though they did—as though the permissiveness thought to be represented in Matthew 19:9 were so universally understood by first century readers that the other New Testament authors saw no need to put it in writing. Even the permissive interpretations of 1 Corinthians 7 ultimately trace their justification back to this single verse in Matthew's Gospel. In our view, there are two serious problems with giving Matthew 19:9 this much interpretive weight.

First, the New Testament contains five statements that amount to unqualified prohibitions of divorce and five statements that amount to unqualified prohibitions of remarriage after divorce (if a former spouse is living). Here are those passages once again:

Prohibitions of Divorce

What therefore God has joined together, let no man separate. (Matt. 19:6; Mark 10:9)

The wife should not leave her husband. (1 Cor. 7:10)

The husband should not divorce his wife. (1 Cor. 7:11)

If any brother has a wife who is an unbeliever, and she consents to live with him, he must not divorce her. (1 Cor. 7:12)

A woman who has an unbelieving husband, and he consents to live with her, she must not send her husband away. (1 Cor. 7:13)

Prohibitions of Remarriage After Divorce

Whoever marries a divorced woman commits adultery. (Matt. 5:32b)

Whoever divorces his wife and marries another woman commits adultery against her; and if she herself divorces her husband and marries another man, she is committing adultery. (Mark 10:11-12)

Everyone who divorces his wife and marries another commits adultery, and he who marries one who is divorced from a husband commits adultery. (Luke 16:18)

So then, if while her husband is living she is joined to another man, she shall be called an adulteress; but if her husband dies, she is free from the law, so that she is not an adulteress though she is joined to another man. (Rom. 7:3)

The wife should not leave her husband (but if she does leave, she must remain unmarried, or else be reconciled to her husband). (1 Cor. 7:10-11a)

The question we are asking is this: Is it a sound interpretive practice to use Matthew 19:9 as the key to explaining what is "missing" in these other ten statements when they are all plainly worded and seem to need no explaining? In each case, either divorce is categorically prohibited or remarriage to a different person after divorce is categorically disallowed (if a former spouse is living).

We are aware that these ten statements are drawn from only five instances of biblical teaching on divorce and remarriage: Jesus' sermon in Matthew 5-7; the Matthew 19/Mark 10 divorce debate; Jesus' instructions in Luke 16:18; Paul's letter to the Romans; Paul's first letter to the Corinthians. Viewed in this way, one might choose to emphasize the fact that two of these five bodies of instruction include the exception clause (i.e., the sermon in Matthew 5-7 and the Matthew 19/Mark 10 divorce debate). Looking at Jesus' teaching alone, one might even point out that He included the clause in two of three instances where His teaching on divorce and remarriage is recorded. This may initially seem to be a weighty factor in opposition to the point we are making here, but before overemphasizing this point, one should carefully consider the weight given to the exception clause by the writers of Scripture, all of whom were recording the "breathed-out" words of God with the perfect balance and proportion intended by the Holy Spirit.

- Mark omits the clause entirely when recording an instance where it *was* spoken by Jesus.

- Luke's account contains no exception clause, indicating either that Jesus Himself omitted it here, or that Luke, like Mark, recognized that it could be omitted while still capturing the intent of Jesus' instructions.

- Paul makes no reference to an exception clause in either of his letters to the churches where divorce and remarriage are discussed, even when he specifically says he is reflecting the Lord's teaching on divorce and remarriage (1 Cor. 7:10-11).

In our view, the fact that these authors omitted the exception clause, while at the same time categorically prohibiting divorce and remarriage, strengthens our position. Furthermore, as we will suggest in the next chapter, Matthew's inclusion of the clause in writing to a uniquely Jewish audience confirms its limited application.

Second, commentators generally agree that of the divorce/ remarriage passages in the New Testament, Matthew 19:9 is the most difficult to interpret conclusively. There are at least seven historically significant interpretations of Matthew 19:9 with its somewhat ambiguous wording, and no small amount of disagreement among reputable Bible scholars as to which one is correct. Five of the seven affirm a no-divorce understanding of the text, and six of them affirm a no-remarriage view. Only one permits both divorce and remarriage. This is not to say that these seven views are equally tempting to all interpreters. Several have serious (and we believe obvious) weaknesses.[8] But it does show that Matthew 19:9 has historically represented a difficult interpretive problem. Therefore, the practice of using the most permissive interpretation of the most ambiguous text as the interpretive key for understanding all the other divorce/remarriage passages in the New Testament is not merely unreliable, it goes directly against one of the most basic rules of biblical interpretation. Lorraine Boettner puts it like this:

> Since the Bible is the Word of God it is self-consistent. Consequently if we find a passage which in itself is capable of two interpretations, one of which harmonizes with the rest of the Scriptures while the other does not, we are duty bound to accept the former. It is a recognized principle of interpretation that the more obscure passages are to be interpreted in the light of clearer passages, and not vice versa.[9]

Rather than pressing the uncertain meaning of Matthew 19:9 on all the other passages, thus permitting both divorce and remarriage in cases of adultery, it is better to shine the interpretative light in

---

8 Abel Isaksson provides a helpful overview of these views in *Marriage and Ministry in the New Temple* (Ejnar Munksgaard Copenhagen: C.W.K. Gleerup Lund, 1965,128-142). Several of these views are discussed in detail by William A. Heth and Gordon J. Wenham in *Jesus and Divorce: The Problem with the Evangelical Consensus* (Nashville: ThomasNelson Publishers, 1985).

9 Lorraine Boettner, *The Reformed Doctrine of Predestination* (Phillipsburg: Presbyterian and Reformed Publishing Co., 1932), 295-296.

the opposite direction. When this principle is employed—when the ambiguity of Matthew 19:9 is subjected to the clarity of all the other passages—it becomes evident that initiating a divorce is never lawful, and remarriage to a different person after divorce (while a former spouse is living) is adultery. Even if one were to remain perpetually unsure of precisely how to interpret Matthew 19:9, the preponderance of evidence found in the other passages should lead to this conclusion.

6

The Meaning of the Exception Clause: What is Porneia?

In his commentary on Matthew's Gospel, D. A. Carson paraphrases Matthew 19:9 this way:

> Anyone who divorces his wife and marries another woman commits adultery—though this principle does not hold in the case of *porneia*.[10]

We believe Carson's paraphrase accurately depicts the function of the exception clause in the sentence. Divorce followed by remarriage is adultery, except in the case of *porneia*. But the question remains, "What is *porneia*?" The biggest controversy related to Matthew 5:32 and 19:9 centers around the meaning of this Greek word. We believe Matthew's (actually Jesus') choice of this particular word proves that the exception clause was never intended to permit divorce in the context of a consummated marriage. Jesus did not use *porneia* in this instance to refer to adultery, but rather as a specific reference to premarital sexual immorality. By using this particular word shortly after prohibiting all divorce in the context of a consummated marriage (Matt. 19:6, Mark 10:9), Jesus made it known that even though He was prohibiting the most common type of divorce categorically (i.e., the dissolution of a consummated union), He was permitting another well-known kind of "divorce" (i.e., the termination of a betrothal arrangement) in cases of premarital sexual sin (*porneia*).[11]

---

10 D. A. Carson, "Matthew," in *The Expositor's Bible Commentary*, ed. Frank E. Gaebelein, (Grand Rapids: Zondervan, 1984), 8:416.

11 To avoid giving the wrong impression, we would note that D. A. Carson does not share our opinion about the restricted meaning of porneia in the exception clause.

This understanding of the exception clause has historically been called "the betrothal view."

Betrothal in First-century Israel

Betrothal for first-century Jews was in some ways similar to the modern practice of engagement. It was the relationship between a man and a woman who were promised to each other in marriage. But there are significant differences between first century Jewish betrothal laws and the modern practice of engagement.

Today the terms "fiancé" and "fiancée" are used to describe an engaged couple. For first century Jews, the betrothal relationship was such that the man and woman were commonly thought of as married and referred to as "husband" and "wife," though their union had not yet been finalized by a marriage ceremony and sexual intercourse. More importantly, in most modern cultures, the separation of an engagement requires no legal procedure. Either party may simply decide not to go through with the marriage. In first-century Jewish culture, however, betrothal was a legally binding contract, often involving significant financial obligations. Partly because of this "business" aspect of betrothal, to nullify the contract prior to the valid consummation of the marriage "required the issuing of a formal divorce."[12] The terms "send away" or "put away" were often used to describe this legal action (cf. Matt. 1:19). Most importantly, the commonly recognized ground for such a divorce was the discovery that one partner had committed the sin of fornication (i.e., premarital sexual immorality). This is precisely what Joseph initially assumed had happened with Mary.

> Now the birth of Jesus Christ was as follows: when His mother Mary had been betrothed to Joseph, before they came together she was found to be with child by the Holy Spirit. And Joseph *her husband*, being a righteous man and not wanting to disgrace her, planned to *send her away* [i.e., divorce her] secretly. (Matt. 1:18-19, emphasis added).

Even before Mary and Joseph had consummated their marriage, he was thought of as "her husband" and she as his "wife" (Matt.

---

12 Andreas J. Kostenberger with David W. Jones, *God, Marriage, and Family: Rebuilding the Biblical Foundation* (Wheaton: Crossway Books, 2004), 184.

1:19-20). In Luke 2:5, Mary is described literally as "betrothed to Joseph." Some modern translations render the phrase, "promised in marriage to him" (NET), or "engaged to him" (NASB). These translations are misleading. The original language calls to mind significantly more than the terms "promised" or "engaged" mean to modern readers. Interestingly, while the NASB translates Luke 2:5 as "engaged to him," Matthew 1:18 in the same version is rendered, "betrothed to Joseph," though the same Greek word is present in both places. Furthermore, the *New American Standard Bible* marginal notes next to Matthew 1:18 describe betrothal as "The first stage of marriage in Jewish culture, usually lasting for a year before the wedding night, more legal than an engagement."[13] The NET Bible includes the comment that the description of Joseph and Mary's betrothal relationship "may suggest that the marriage is not yet consummated, [but] not necessarily that they are not currently married"[14] In the eyes of Jewish culture, Joseph and Mary *were* married in nearly every sense (including the legal sense), with the only exceptions being the final ceremony and the consummation through sexual intercourse. Once this is understood, it makes sense to say that the dissolution of a betrothal arrangement would be called a "divorce."

The sin Joseph believed Mary to be guilty of (that is, before the angel appeared to him and informed him of the real situation) was not the sin of adultery, but fornication. Adultery can only occur in the context of a consummated marriage, and Joseph and Mary had not yet consummated their marriage sexually. Joseph clearly knew that according to existing Jewish law, he not only had the legal right to divorce her, but was expected to do so (that is, if Mary were actually guilty). This is why the angel told Joseph not to be "afraid" to take Mary as his wife (Matt. 1:20). As Abel Isaksson explains,

> A man was not considered to have acted justly if he did not bring forward any complaints he might have about his wife's not being a virgin. He had to report these complaints to the municipal court and divorce her. This rule seems to have been almost as binding as that which stated that a man could not

---

13 *New American Standard Bible*, Side-Column Reference Edition (Anaheim: Foundation Publications, 1996), NT, 1.

14 The NET Bible, New English Translation (Biblical Studies Press, L.L.C., 1996-2003), 1795.

forgive his wife any act of adultery she might commit but was compelled to divorce her.[15]

Matthew referred to Joseph as "a righteous man" in verse 19, not because he wanted to avoid shaming Mary (as is commonly assumed), but rather because he was planning to do what existing Jewish law prescribed. In all likelihood, verse 19 should be understood as saying, "Joseph, being a righteous, law-abiding man, intended to divorce Mary as the law prescribed. Yet also being compassionate and not wanting to disgrace her, he determined to carry out the lawful and socially expected divorce in secret."[16]

By the time of Christ, the death penalty was not commonly enforced in cases of premarital sexual immorality (as prescribed in Deuteronomy 22:20-21). It had been replaced over the centuries by a law which provided for the legal termination of the betrothal obligation. Though this in some ways resembles what we would now call an annulment, it was called "divorce" in Jewish legal literature, and these types of divorces were not uncommon. First century Jewish law even required marriages to virgins to take place on the fourth day of the week because the courts that decided betrothal divorce cases sat in session on the fifth day of the week. This way, cases of premarital unchastity that were discovered on the wedding night could be heard immediately.[17]

The Divorce Debate in Light of First-century Betrothal Customs

Consider the divorce debate between Jesus and the Pharisees in light of what we know about first-century Jewish betrothal customs. Jesus answered the Pharisees' initial question about whether or not it was lawful to divorce their wives by saying, "What therefore God has joined together, let no man separate" (Matt. 19:6; Mark 10:9).

---

15 Isaksson, *Marriage and Ministry in the New Temple*, 135-136. Isaksson bases his conclusions on the Jewish document known as "Tractate Ketuvoth," a sub-section of the Jewish Talmud containing 112 regulations regarding marriage, betrothal, divorce, and remarriage.

16 The portion in quotes is our own interpretive restatement. For a detailed defense of this understanding of Matthew 1:19, see Isaksson, *Marriage and Ministry in the New Temple*, 135-139.

17 The way the woman's virginity was confirmed on the wedding night was, of course, through sexual union with her husband (Deut. 22:13-19). Normally, this first sexual union was the consummation of the marriage, but in first century Jewish culture, the marriage was not considered consummated unless the first sexual union proved the woman to be a virgin (i.e., by the evidence of blood). Otherwise, the man betrothed to her was thought to have been defrauded and the betrothal agreement was lawfully terminated the next day.

In saying this He clearly prohibited divorce in the context of a consummated marriage. Knowing Jewish betrothal law, however, He proceeded to qualify His otherwise unqualified prohibition by allowing for divorce in cases of unfaithfulness during the betrothal period, calling this specific situation *porniea* (fornication).

Jesus added the phrase, "except for immorality [*porneia*]" in the encounter with the Pharisees (Matt. 19:9), and the phrase, "except for the reason of unchastity [*porneia*]" in the Sermon on the Mount (Matt. 5:32), to avoid a misunderstanding. He was not permitting divorce in cases of adultery (*moicheia*, which, of course, can only occur in the context of a consummated marriage). He was permitting divorce (or what we might now call an annulment) in cases like that described in Deuteronomy 22:20-21, when a betrothal agreement had been violated by premarital sexual immorality (*porneia*). Since the separation of a betrothal relationship due to premarital sexual immorality was considered a legal divorce, Jesus did not want to be accused of teaching the Jews that even if a man found his *betrothed* wife to be unchaste he was compelled to go through with the marriage. In this particular situation, as Jesus made clear by including the exception clauses, the betrayed man was free from any obligation to have her as his wife. She had committed *porneia* (fornication) and he was permitted to divorce her. But Jesus said nothing to indicate that once a man and a woman consummated their union as husband and wife—once they had become one flesh, in other words— the man was permitted to divorce his wife (or vice versa) under certain conditions.

In further support of the betrothal view we offer the following four points:

1. Matthew is the only gospel writer who includes the exception clause (5:32; 19:9). He is also the only one who describes Joseph's intent to divorce Mary, which, as Matthew indicates, was the righteous thing for Joseph to do. Since Matthew is the only one who describes Joseph and the situation in this way, it logically follows that Matthew would be the one to include the fact that divorce in these specific situations was not unlawful. Otherwise, without the exception clause, Jesus would be seen as prohibiting an action which Matthew had earlier referred to as righteous.

2. According to nearly universal scholarly opinion, Matthew's Gospel was intended for a primarily Jewish audience. His purpose was to convince Jews that Jesus was the Messiah, their King. Since Jews in particular would understand Jewish betrothal laws and would therefore wonder if Jesus were prohibiting even *this* type of divorce, it would naturally follow that Matthew would be the one to include the exception clause.

Mark and Luke, on the other hand, were writing primarily to Greek and Roman readers who, being less familiar with Jewish marriage laws, would not have easily associated the term "divorce" with anything other than the termination of a consummated marriage. Therefore, Mark and Luke saw no need to include the exception clause when they recorded Jesus' teaching about divorce and remarriage (Mark 10:11-12; Luke 16:18). They may have even recognized that including the phrase, "except for immorality," would mislead their readers into thinking that Jesus was allowing an exception to His no-divorce, no-remarriage teaching in the context of a consummated marriage. They may have omitted the exception clause in order to *preserve* Jesus' intention to disallow all divorce (as divorce was commonly understood among non-Jews).

3. Matthew's usage of the word *porneia* (fornication) seems to be very specific and limited in its meaning. He uses *porneia* three times:

> But I say to you that everyone who divorces his wife, except for the reason of *unchastity* [*porneia*], makes her *commit adultery* [a verb form of *moicheia*]. (5:32)

> For out of the heart come evil thoughts, murders, *adulteries* [plural of *moicheia*], *fornications* [plural of *porneia*], thefts, false witnesses, slanders. (15:19)

> And I say to you, whoever divorces his wife, except for *immorality* [*porneia*], and marries another woman *commits adultery* [a verb form of *moicheia*]. (19:9).

Notice that each time Matthew uses *porneia* (fornication), he also uses either *moicheia* (adultery) or a verb form of *moicheia* in the same sentence. This at least suggests that Matthew did not see the two words as having the same meaning. This factor alone would not be conclusive, however, were it not for the fact that in 15:19 he places the two words, both in noun form, next to each other in a list of various types of sins that proceed out of the human heart. Here it is *impossible* to conclude that Matthew saw them as meaning the same thing. He obviously recognized that for his readership, the two words would have called to mind two distinct types of sin. Given the clear distinction of the two words in Matthew 15:19, it would be hard to explain why Matthew would not have chosen to use *moicheia* instead of *porneia* in the exception clause if he were describing sexual immorality in a consummated marriage (which is *always* adultery). Where he describes the sin of adultery elsewhere, he always chooses *moicheia* (or its verb form), not *porneia* (cf. 5:27, 28, 31; 15:19; 19:18). It is important to note that two of Matthew's uses of the verb form of *moicheia* to denote "adultery" immediately precede the use of *porneia* in the exception clause in 5:32. The fact is, if the sin of adultery were what Jesus intended to describe in the exception clause, *moicheia* would have more clearly explained His meaning and would have been more consistent with Matthew's writing pattern.

4. In John's Gospel the word *porneia* (fornication) is only used once, in John 8:41. To understand the context in which the word was used, note that Jesus had just challenged the Pharisees' claim that they were children of Abraham (vv. 39-40). In verse 44 He calls them children of the devil. In the midst of this heated conversation, the Pharisees replied, "We were not born of fornication [*porneia*]; we have one Father: God" (v. 41).

The unbelieving Pharisees clearly could not allow themselves to believe that Jesus was actually born of a virgin. After all, if they were to admit that He was born in this way, it would be very difficult to then deny that He was the fulfillment of the virgin birth prophecy in Isaiah

7:14, which would also make Him the fulfillment of Isaiah 9:6-7, Daniel 7:13-14, and Micah 5:2. In other words, the virgin birth served as proof that Jesus was the King of the Jews who was to sit forever on the throne of David. So they *had* to deny the virgin birth. But the only way to deny Jesus' virgin birth was to claim that Mary had gotten pregnant as the result of sexual intercourse with Joseph (or some other man) prior to the marriage being legitimately consummated. This would have made Jesus one who was "born of fornication [*porneia*]." The point is, the Pharisees' use of the word *porneia* to describe what they perceived as Mary's premarital sexual activity seems to indicate that this single word was commonly understood by first-century Jews to describe the particular sin of premarital sex, not the sin of adultery. This is further affirmed by the fact that in the Septuagint, or Greek translation of the Old Testament, the word used in Deuteronomy 22:21 to describe premarital sexual sin is a derivative of *porneia*.[18]

When all of these factors are considered, it seems certain to us that when Jesus said, "Whoever divorces his wife, except for *porneia*," He was not permitting divorce in the context of a consummated marriage. Instead, He was clarifying that His categorical prohibition of divorce did not apply when one party to a betrothal agreement was found to have been unchaste prior to the consummation of the marriage. Jesus was saying that in these situations, the formal dissolution of the betrothal union was lawful.

The question has been asked, "Because the Jews used 'divorce' terminology to refer to the dissolution of betrothal arrangements, would the betrothed person who was 'divorced' in this way be permitted to marry someone else? In other words, does Jesus' general prohibition of remarriage after divorce mean that even *this* 'divorced' person would commit adultery if he or she remarried?" Since no consummated marriage was formed in these situations, no one-flesh union was created, therefore the issue of re-marriage after a betrothal divorce was not applicable. The issue of remarriage after a betrothal divorce was not even addressed in Jesus' instructions. His only reference to the betrothal situation was in the exception

---

18 Isaksson, *Marriage and Ministry in the New Temple*, 135.

clause itself, with the rest of the passage, including the prohibition of remarriage after divorce, referring exclusively to divorce in the context of a consummated marriage. The man and woman whose betrothal contract was legally ended by "divorce" were free to marry someone else.

7

Responding to Four Objections
to the Betrothal View

In our study of various positions held by conservative, Bible-believing evangelicals, we have found that there are four primary objections to a no-divorce, no-remarriage view in general, and/or to the betrothal view specifically.[19] The following section explains these arguments against our position, as well as our reasons for not finding them compelling.

Objection 1: Those who hold the betrothal view believe the word *porneia* in the exception clause is limited to premarital sexual unfaithfulness and does not include other sexual sins like adultery. The word *porneia* should not be given such a narrow meaning. It must be allowed to refer to a broader range of sexual sins, including adultery.

Our Response: We would agree that *porneia* is not always limited in this way in the New Testament. Paul uses it at times to refer to sexual sin in general (e.g., 1 Cor. 6:18; Gal. 5:19). But even outside the Gospels, *pornos* (fornicator, one who engages in *porneia*) is plainly distinguished from *moichos* (adulterer, one who engages in *moicheia*) as two different categories of sinners (e.g., 1 Cor. 6:9; Heb. 13:4). Also, the New Testament writers commonly gave the same word varying nuances in meaning to suit different circumstances. While every word has a range of meaning, the specific meaning of a word must be determined by the context in

---

19 There are other objections, but these four came up most often in the course of our study and in our discussions with others.

which it is used. Therefore, with respect to Matthew's use of *porneia* in 5:32 and 19:9, we must consider the following:

- Matthew's Gospel is the only example we have of his writing. There are no other places for interpreters to look in order to answer the question, "How did Matthew use *porneia*?"[20]

- In Matthew 15:19, *porneia* and *moicheia* are separated as two of seven sins that Jesus says proceed out of the human heart. Therefore it is not only allowable, but necessary to conclude that Matthew did not see these two words as having the same meaning. Given this usage in 15:19, it is highly unlikely, since Matthew also distinguishes *porneia* from the verb form of *moicheia* in the exception clauses, that He saw them as having the same meaning (or even overlapping meanings) in these cases.

- Matthew was writing to Jewish readers who would have had a well-ingrained concept of betrothal divorce. Therefore, the betrothal understanding of *porneia* fits the historical context of Matthew's Gospel in particular.

- The betrothal understanding of *porneia* in Matthew 5:32 and 19:9 harmonizes with the rest of the divorce/remarriage texts in the New Testament.

Additionally, Luke never uses *porneia* in his Gospel. Mark only uses it once (7:21), and in that single instance the word is distinguished from adultery (*moicheia*) in the same sentence, just as in Matthew 15:19. John's single use of the word seems to be a reference to premarital sexual immorality (John 8:41). The point is, within the context of the four Gospels, the weight of evidence not only permits, but *favors* giving the word a restricted meaning—in this case, one that does not include the sin of adultery. In our view there are simply no compelling reasons *not* to limit the meaning of *porneia* in Matthew 5:32 and 19:9 to premarital sexual immorality.

---

20 Matthew was quoting Jesus, so it is not technically Matthew's use of *porneia* that we are concerned about. But since Matthew never uses *porneia* except when quoting Jesus, it is obvious that Matthew's intent in using the word is always the same as Jesus' intent. In other words, it is just as accurate to say "Matthew's use of *porneia*" as it is to say "Jesus' use of *porneia*."

We would also point out that most who object to our narrow meaning of *porneia* restrict the meaning of the word themselves. By insisting that *porneia* in the exception clause refers to sexual immorality in the context of a consummated marriage, they limit the meaning of *porneia* to adultery only, since it is generally agreed that sexual immorality in a consummated marriage is *always* adultery.[21] In this way they rule out premarital sex as one possible meaning of *porneia* in Matthew 5:32 and 19:9. Furthermore, unless they are willing to say that any type of adultery provides grounds for divorce, even a single lustful glance at another woman (cf. Matt. 5:28), their meaning of *porneia* in the exception clause becomes even narrower. It is not merely limited to the sin of adultery, but to adultery in its more serious physical forms.[22] In the final analysis, the same interpreters who insist on the broadest definition of *porneia* in Matthew 5:32 and 19:9 end up with a definition that is just as restricted as ours, though in a different way. The important difference between their position and ours is that they limit the meaning of the word in their favor without the contextual support of the way it is consistently used in the Gospels.

Objection 2: The betrothal view leads to the conclusion that initiating a divorce is always unlawful in the context of a consummated marriage. But this cannot be harmonized with God's divorce of Israel for her adulteries. If the betrothal view (or any other no-divorce view) is correct, God sinned.

Our Response: There are two places in the Old Testament where it is clearly stated that God divorced Israel. One of these passages specifies that Israel's "adulteries" were the reason for the divorce, indicating that a consummated marriage was in view.

> Thus says the Lord, "Where is the certificate of divorce by which I have sent your mother away? Or to whom of My creditors did I sell you? Behold, you were sold for your iniquities, and for your transgressions your mother was sent away." (Is. 50:1)

---

21 As John MacArthur writes, for example, "In the context of marriage [porneia] always constituted adultery, which, by definition, is illicit sex by a married person." John MacArthur, *The MacArthur New Testament Commentary: Matthew 16-23* (Chicago: Moody Press, 1988), 171.

22 We are glad that most who permit divorce for adultery discourage it strongly in all but the most serious cases, but the restriction of divorce to "physical forms of adultery only" is arbitrary and without scriptural justification.

And I saw that for all the adulteries of faithless Israel, I
had sent her away and given her a writ of divorce, yet her
treacherous sister Judah did not fear; but she went and was a
harlot also. (Jer. 3:8)

These two verses are commonly appealed to when arguing that God
condones divorce when it is for the reason of a spouse's adultery.
Since God divorced His unfaithful "wife," we certainly ought to be
permitted to follow His example in similar circumstances (or so the
reasoning goes). We believe there are at least four factors that prove
this reasoning unsound.

1. God's "marriage" to Israel, as well as the "divorce," were
   metaphorical. There was never an actual marriage or an
   actual certificate of divorce. God simply used these familiar
   images and terms to illustrate the nature of Israel's evil and
   of His divine judgment. While it is valid to use descriptions
   of common Jewish divorce practices to illustrate the nature
   of Israel's sin and God's judgment, it is not necessarily
   valid to rely on metaphorical illustrations of Israel's sin
   (i.e., metaphorical adultery) and God's judgment (i.e.,
   metaphorical divorce) when determining acceptable
   practice. Biblical metaphors, while helpful in illustrating,
   should not be heavily relied upon for doctrinal teaching.
   This principle will be explained clearly in number 2.

2. Some of the Bible's metaphorical descriptions of God's
   marriage to Israel are obviously *not* reliable determiners
   of acceptable practice. For example, both Jeremiah and
   Ezekiel portray God as being married to two sisters at
   the same time (Jer. 3:8-10; Ezek. 23). Both metaphorical
   sisters bore children to the Lord (Ezek. 23:1-4), proving
   that both "marriages" were fully consummated. But
   polygamy is intolerable in the New Testament (1 Cor.
   7:2-4) and was never God's original plan for marriage
   (Gen. 2:24). Additionally, both metaphorical sisters were
   daughters of the same metaphorical mother (Eze. 23:2).
   Their mother was the original nation of Israel, which was
   later divided into two kingdoms (i.e., Israel and Judah, the
   two metaphorical sisters). This paints a picture of marriage

that is in direct violation of Leviticus 18:17, "You shall not uncover the nakedness of a woman and of her daughter" (cf. Lev. 20:14). God did not intend for His people to pattern their marital behavior after the metaphorical descriptions of His relationship with these two sisters and their mother.

3. The New Testament shows the "marriage" between God and His people in a totally new light. Although every believer is joined to Christ at conversion, the final marriage of Christ and His bride (i.e., the church) is yet future. In Ephesians 5:25-27, we are told that the bride of Christ is being prepared for the wedding. Christ intends to present her to Himself "in all her glory, having no spot or wrinkle or any such thing; but that she would be holy and blameless" (v. 27). This marriage will only be consummated when Christ, the Bridegroom, returns for His fully prepared bride (Matt. 25:1-13; Rev. 19:7-9). So while the Old Testament nation of Israel was frequently described in terms that would call to mind a fully consummated marriage (e.g., Jer. 3:8; Eze. 23:1-4), the New Testament portrays God's chosen people (some of whom are old covenant Jews) as betrothed to Christ but not yet fully married to Him.

4. Paul opens Romans 11 with the question, "God has not rejected His people, has He?" His answer comes like this: "May it never be! . . . God has not rejected His people whom He foreknew" (vv. 1-2a). Paul's clear intent is to cause the reader to realize that God would *never* do such a thing because it would be a violation of a divine promise. And as he continues in Romans 11, one comes to see that the most that can be taken from the metaphorical divorce texts in the Old Testament is that the divorce of Israel was partial. *Some* of the branches of the olive tree were broken off (v. 17), but the tree itself was preserved. Whatever eschatological position one holds about the future of the physical nation of Israel, there is no way to harmonize this text with a total divorce of Israel in the Old Testament. Even in the Old Testament texts, God divorced only one of the two sisters (i.e., Israel, the apostate northern kingdom).

Never is it explicitly stated that He divorced Judah, even though she became more immoral than her sister (Jer. 3:1-11; Eze. 23:11). There was indeed a metaphorical divorce, but it was not of the original nation of Israel in any universal sense. And since it is impossible for a person to partially divorce his or her spouse, the metaphorical divorce texts are once again shown to be unreliable determiners of acceptable behavior in terms of marriage, divorce, and remarriage.

Objection 3: Paul's statement in 1 Corinthians 7:25, "Now concerning virgins I have no command of the Lord," proves that Jesus said nothing whatsoever about virgins or betrothal situations.

Our Response: This objection misses the point of Paul's statement entirely. Paul was answering a question about whether or not a betrothed (never-married) person should marry or stay single. Jesus gave no instructions whatsoever that would serve as an answer to this question (unlike 1 Corinthians 10-11 where Paul paraphrased Jesus' comprehensive doctrine of divorce and remarriage). Also, the exception clauses in Matthew 5:32 and 19:9 are not given in the form of commands to those who are betrothed. They are *exceptions* to the commands not to divorce or remarry after divorce. Paul's assertion that he had no *command* from the Lord concerning the specific betrothal questions in Corinth in no way implies that Jesus never spoke about betrothal.

Objection 4: The Pharisees' question in Matthew 19:3 and Mark 10:2 concerns divorce in the context of a consummated marriage, not betrothal. Furthermore, nothing is said either prior to or after the exception clause to indicate that Jesus was referring to betrothal in Matthew 19:9.

Our Response: It is true that the Pharisees were asking about divorce in the context of a consummated marriage. It is also true that when Jesus said, "What therefore God has joined together, let no man separate," He was prohibiting the termination of a consummated marriage, not a betrothal arrangement. We agree that there is nothing in the surrounding context to indicate that Jesus was giving instructions related to betrothal. But if the word *porneia* refers to premarital sexual immorality, as we believe it does in Matthew's Gospel, betrothal does not need to be mentioned in the surrounding context in order to be the legitimate subject of the exception clause. In fact, one should expect that an exception to a rule might not necessarily be a part of the main topic of conversation when the rule itself is being discussed.

For example, if we were discussing traffic laws with a police officer, we might ask him, "Is it ever lawful to drive in excess of 200 miles-per-hour?" His response might be, "Any person who drives in excess of 200 miles-per-hour, except for a race car driver on a closed track, is breaking the law." Even though the subject of discussion was lawful behavior on public roads, it would not seem strange for the officer to insert a reference to race car driving as an obvious, though somewhat unrelated, exception. Similarly, even though the subject of the divorce debate was the termination of a consummated marriage, it should not seem strange for Jesus to insert a reference to betrothal divorce as an obvious, though somewhat unrelated, exception. In this case, Jesus had an important reason for inserting it. Given the Pharisees' desire to cause trouble for Him, along with the broad meaning of "divorce" in first-century Israel, the exception clause was necessary in order to affirm the continuing legality of betrothal divorce, and to preclude any later misrepresentation of His teaching.

8

The Historical and Biblical Context for the Divorce Debate

If one hopes to discover what was meant by a particular statement, in the Bible or anywhere else, it is necessary to understand the context in which it was made. The statement we are examining here is one made by Jesus in the context of a debate about divorce. He said, "And I say to you, whoever divorces his wife, except for immorality, and marries another woman commits adultery" (Matt. 19:9).

The purpose of this chapter is to ask, and hopefully answer, the question, "What was happening when Jesus made this statement?" This general question branches out into several more specific ones:

- What were the acceptable standards for divorce and remarriage in Israel prior to Christ's ministry?

- Who were the men who confronted Jesus with the question about divorce?

- Why did these particular men seek Him out to ask their question?

- What was Jesus' typical way of responding to questions from Jewish religious leaders?

- What relationship does this debate have with Jesus' prior teaching on divorce and remarriage in the Sermon on the Mount?"

It is our hope that by providing reasonable, contextually justifiable answers to these questions, we will help the reader to understand better the meaning of Matthew 19:9. More specifically, we hope to show that the commonly accepted interpretation of Jesus' statement is sharply at odds with the context in which it was made. Please read this chapter carefully. This may be the most important chapter in the book.

The Pharisees' Disagreement with Each Other

It is widely agreed that in Jesus' time there were two differing schools of thought among the Pharisees regarding divorce and remarriage. The differing positions were based on a disagreement as to how the Hebrew word translated "indecency" in Deuteronomy 24:1 should be interpreted, along with the mistaken opinion that Deuteronomy 24:1 gave active permission to divorce a wife. The school of Hillel taught that a man could divorce his wife for nearly anything he chose to label as "indecency," even something as trivial as "an improperly cooked meal."[23] The more conservative school of Shammai "interpreted the expression to refer to gross indecency," which generally meant sexual indecency, but possibly included actions that fell short of adultery.[24] Both groups taught that if a man divorced his wife for "valid" reasons, the man and the woman were free to remarry, as is well-documented in Jewish divorce records.[25]

The Audience with Jesus in the Matthew 19/Mark 10 Divorce Debate

We do not know specifically who the men were who confronted Jesus in the Matthew19/Mark 10 encounter. We do know that they were Pharisees, so it is reasonable to conclude that they were aware of the two differing schools of thought. We do not know which of the two views were represented by these particular men, however, or if both views were represented.

---

23 Carson, "Matthew," in *The Expositor's Bible Commentary*, 8:411.

24 Ibid.

25 David Instone-Brewer, *Divorce and Remarriage in the Bible* (Grand Rapids: Eerdman's, 2002), 20-33. Instone-Brewer's research into pre-Christian Jewish divorce practices is helpful, but in stark contrast with the New Testament, he allows for divorce in almost any undesirable marital situation, and remarriage after any divorce. For this reason we cannot commend his work any further than for his analysis of pre-Christian marriage and divorce practices. For further information, see the online review of Instone-Brewer's book by Daryl Wingerd at www.CCWtoday.org.

Therefore, we should not *automatically* conclude (as many interpreters do) that Jesus was being asked to give His opinion as to which view was correct. Even if we did know that representatives from both groups were present and were asking Jesus to decide between their two opinions, the logical flow of the debate should move interpreters away from concluding that He simply sided with the more conservative group. The flow of thought should lead to the conclusion that He rejected Pharisaical opinions altogether and returned everyone to God's ideal for marriage as originally stated in Genesis 2:24. Let's look at the first part of the passage in Matthew's Gospel.

> Some Pharisees came to Jesus, testing Him and asking, "Is it lawful for a man to divorce his wife for any reason at all?" And He answered and said, "Have you not read that He who created them from the beginning made them male and female, and said, 'For this reason a man shall leave his father and mother and be joined to his wife, and the two shall become one flesh'? So they are no longer two, but one flesh. What therefore God has joined together, let no man separate." They said to Him, "Why then did Moses command to give her a certificate of divorce and send her away?" He said to them, "Because of your hardness of heart Moses permitted you to divorce your wives; but from the beginning it has not been this way. And I say to you, whoever divorces his wife, except for immorality, and marries another woman commits adultery." (Matt. 19:3-9)

The Intent of the Question Itself: Seeking Harmony Between Matthew and Mark

Some interpreters claim that the way in which the Pharisees' question is recorded in Matthew's account ("Is it lawful for a man to divorce his wife *for any reason at all*?" emphasis added) proves that they were wondering whether Jesus would say that any *trivial* reason was sufficient to justify divorce (as the school of Hillel taught), or that divorce was restricted to sexual indecency (as the school of Shammai taught). If this understanding of the intent of the Pharisees' question is correct, Jesus' response in verse 9 might be more easily seen as an affirmation of the Shammai position, which permitted divorce and remarriage in cases of adultery. But even if this were the intent of the Pharisees' question, it would still fail to account for Jesus' unqualified prohibition of divorce in verse 6 and His reaffirmation of that prohibition in verse 8. In other words, whether the Pharisees were asking for His decision between limited divorce and unrestricted divorce, or asking if divorce is *ever* lawful, Jesus answered in a way that disallowed divorce altogether.

More importantly, Mark's paraphrased rendering of the Pharisees' question seems to clarify its true intent. According to Mark, they came to Jesus asking "whether it was lawful for a man to divorce a wife" (Mark 10:2). Mark leaves out the words, "for any reason at all." This indicates that these five words were not necessary in order to understand the heart of the question. If the Pharisees *were* hoping Jesus would settle a dispute between their two views, then the words "for any reason at all" are critical. Mark would have omitted wording that is necessary in order to understand the encounter correctly, and his paraphrase would actually mislead the reader. But if the Pharisees were asking whether divorce is *ever* lawful (as we believe to be the case), Mark's abbreviated version makes perfect sense. The Pharisees were not asking whether or not divorce is allowable for certain trivial reasons, but whether or not divorce is allowable for any reason. To this question, Jesus answered, "No."

The Pharisees' Motives

When Jewish religious leaders asked Jesus questions, it was not typically because they valued His opinion. They asked Him questions because they hoped His answers would either damage His credibility with the people or get Him in trouble with the authorities. This motive is consistently exhibited in the Gospels. For example, the Pharisees were not seeking to be morally upright in their financial dealings when they asked Jesus about paying taxes to Caesar. Instead, the text tells us that they "plotted together how they might trap Him in what He said" (Matt. 22:15).

The text of the divorce debate is just as revealing. We are told at the outset of the debate that these men came "testing" Jesus (Matt. 19:3; Mark 10:2). They did not come with honest or noble motives. They did not hope to learn from Him. They wanted to get Him into trouble. As we noted earlier, first century Jewish law *required* divorce for adultery,[26] so for Jesus to *permit* divorce in these cases

---

26 See Abel Isaksson's statement referenced in footnote 15.

would have been nothing new or surprising. It would not have gotten Him into trouble, in other words. What would have been surprising—what would have likely damaged His credibility with the people and/or caused trouble with Jewish and Roman authorities—was for Him to disallow *all* divorce in the context of a consummated marriage. [27]

Jesus' Pattern: Out with the Pharisaical Old, In with the Challenging New

Jesus' pattern, from the beginning of His ministry, was to call His followers to a higher standard of righteousness than that which was commonly expected among Jews—a higher standard than even that of the Pharisees. In the Sermon on the Mount, He said to them, "unless your righteousness surpasses that of the scribes and Pharisees, you will not enter the kingdom of heaven" (Matt. 5:20). In His ensuing instructions (vv. 21-48), Jesus presented various aspects of Pharisaical teaching while countering six times with the authoritative phrase, "But I say to you . . . ." Jesus was at least elevating these commonly accepted interpretations of the Old Testament, if not totally rejecting them and issuing His own new law. It would have been utterly uncharacteristic for Him to have followed this revolutionary body of instruction by merely affirming the more conservative version of the Pharisaical *status quo* in Matthew 19:9.

Throughout Matthew's Gospel Jesus' pattern is to reject Pharisaical teaching altogether, often using derogatory terms. In Matthew 15 He described the Pharisees as "blind guides of the blind" (v. 14), men who were "teaching as doctrines the precepts of men" (v. 9). In Matthew 16 He instructed His disciples to "beware of . . . the teaching of the Pharisees and Sadducees" (v. 12; cf. vv. 5-11). When the Pharisees spoke to Him about marriage as it relates to the resurrection of the dead, He told them that they were "mistaken, not understanding the Scriptures nor the power of God" (Matt. 22:29).

---

27 This encounter took place in Herod's jurisdiction. In Matthew 14:3-12, Matthew records the fact that when John the Baptist spoke out against Herod's unlawful marriage to his brother's wife, Herod had him imprisoned, and eventually beheaded. The Pharisees may have chosen this particular location ("the region of Judea beyond the Jordan," Matt. 19:1, cf. Mark 10:1) to test Jesus concerning divorce and remarriage, hoping that Herod would respond to His teaching in the same way.

And in Matthew 23 He railed against their supposed authority as teachers of the law of God by calling them "blind guides" (v. 16), "fools" (v. 17), and "blind men" (v. 19). Even His initial response to the Pharisees in the Matthew 19 divorce debate was an implicit accusation of ignorance and error on their part. He asked, "Have you not read . . . ?" By responding in this way, Jesus was telling these well-read and highly respected teachers of Israel that their question exposed their failure to rightly understand Moses. Given this pattern of harsh criticism of Pharisaical teaching, it would have been completely uncharacteristic for Jesus to conclude the debate by siding with the more conservative Pharisaical position.

The Connection with the Sermon on the Mount

When all of the above factors in the Matthew 19/Mark 10 divorce debate are considered, the most likely scenario is this: The Pharisees came to Jesus to test Him regarding divorce and remarriage because they had already heard that in the Sermon on the Mount He had repudiated their permissive teaching. They were now daring him to say directly to them what He had said before to his disciples. What Jesus said earlier was this:

> It was said, "Whoever sends his wife away, let him give her a certificate of divorce";[28] but I say to you that everyone who divorces his wife, except for the reason of unchastity, makes her commit adultery; and whoever marries a divorced woman commits adultery. (Matt. 5:31-32)

Based on their misinterpretation of Deuteronomy 24:1, the Pharisees taught that the husband who divorced his wife for "indecency" was justified in doing so *as long as he gave her a certificate of divorce*. As we noted above, Jewish divorce certificates always allowed remarriage, so the woman's second marriage was also condoned in Pharisaical teaching. Jesus countered in Matthew 5:32 by saying that the man who gives his wife a certificate of divorce "makes her commit adultery," and that the second man she marries commits adultery with her. According to Jesus, the

---

28 If Jesus intended to quote from Deuteronomy 24:1 here, the best that could be said is that He quoted the verse quite loosely. It is more likely that He was quoting (or paraphrasing) the common misinterpretation of the passage.

Jewish divorce certificate did nothing to make remarriage after divorce lawful in God's eyes. Remarriage after divorce (which was apparently a social or financial necessity in that culture) was an act of adultery for which the husband who divorced his wife bore a part of the blame, along with the woman herself and her second husband.

Jesus' purpose in Matthew 5:31-32 was not to identify one condition that would justify divorcing a wife in the context of a consummated marriage. His purpose was the same as it was every other time He spoke about divorce and remarriage, to tell His followers that contrary to the commonly accepted teaching, *divorce is an unacceptable breach of God's institution of marriage, and it leads to remarriage, which is adultery.* The exception clause in verse 32 causes confusion when *porneia* is wrongly taken to mean "adultery." But no one can legitimately deny that the main thrust of Jesus' statement was this: "Whoever divorces his wife . . . makes her commit adultery; and whoever marries a divorced woman commits adultery."

If the exception clause in Matthew 5:32 permits divorce in cases of adultery, Jesus' divorce doctrine would not have differed substantially from that of the Shammai Pharisees who *permitted* divorce in the context of a consummated marriage for sexual indecency, and *required* it for adultery. The only major difference between His teaching and theirs would have been His prohibition of remarriage after divorce. With this being the case, one would expect that His prohibition of remarriage would have been the object of their protests in the later encounter. However, in the Matthew 19/Mark 10 debate, their only protest was directed against His prohibition of divorce. Immediately after Jesus said, "What therefore God has joined together, let no man separate," they replied, "Why then did Moses command to give her a certificate of divorce and send her away?" (Matt. 19:6-7). It was Jesus' prohibition of divorce, even without respect to His prohibition of remarriage after divorce, that was totally at odds with the Pharisees' interpretation of Deuteronomy 24:1. The only way the Pharisees' response in Matthew 19 fits with Jesus' earlier teaching is if Jesus prohibited *all* divorce in Matthew 5:32 (with the exception of betrothal divorce). If He had permitted divorce for adultery in the context of a consummated marriage, they would have had no reason to be opposed to His teaching, and therefore no reason to seek Him out to test Him.

If the exception clause refers only to the situation of the betrothal divorce, then Jesus' total repudiation of the Pharisees' interpretation of Deuteronomy 24:1 is perfectly preserved. This is the most reasonable way of interpreting Matthew 5:31-32, partly because Matthew consistently uses the word *porneia* to mean "fornication," not "adultery," and also because this interpretation makes better sense out of the later encounter with the Pharisees.

For the sake of clarity, let us restate what we believe prompted the Matthew 19/Mark 10 encounter: Having learned that Jesus disallowed *all* divorce in the context of a consummated marriage (Matt. 5:31-32), the Pharisees' sought Him out in order to test Him (Matt. 19:3). They were indignant at His earlier complete rejection of their teaching. Therefore they intended to force Him to either repeat it in their presence, and thus be subject to a charge of disregarding Moses, or back away from His rigid teaching in the Sermon on the Mount and thereby become known as one who compromised under pressure. He did the former, of course, boldly maintaining the force of His previous teaching while attributing Moses' passive permissiveness to the hardness of their hearts.

The Disciples' Shocked Response

Just as we can learn much about Jesus' teaching by examining the response it elicited from His enemies, we can also learn by examining the response from His friends.

> The disciples said to Him, "If the relationship of the man with his wife is like this, it is better not to marry." But He said to them, "Not all men can accept this statement, but only those to whom it has been given. For there are eunuchs who were born that way from their mother's womb; and there are eunuchs who were made eunuchs by men; and there are also eunuchs who made themselves eunuchs for the sake of the kingdom of heaven. He who is able to accept this, let him accept it. (Matt. 19:10-12)

If Matthew 19:9 allows for divorce and remarriage in cases of adultery, the disciples' response is nonsensical. When they said, "If the relationship of the man with his wife is like this, it is better not to marry," it would seem clear that they were reflecting on the permanence of the one-flesh union as Jesus had just described it, and on His uncompromising teaching. They would have had no reason to react this way if Jesus were merely agreeing with (or even slightly modifying) a well-known position that permitted both divorce and remarriage. Their amazed (even disgruntled) response would have more naturally followed a complete prohibition of both divorce and remarriage after divorce. Jesus' response concerning eunuchs (vv. 11-12) has long puzzled interpreters, but it at least strongly implies that the disciples' reaction was in some way related to the thought of celibacy. In this context, the only way Jesus could have been teaching about the necessity of celibacy was if He were referring to mandatory celibacy after divorce.

Summary

Both the historical setting and the logical progression of the Matthew 19/Mark 10 debate with the Pharisees argue strongly for understanding Jesus' prohibition of divorce as being without exception in the context of a consummated marriage. To the first-century Jewish reader, the exception clause in Matthew 19:9 would have brought to mind the legal "divorce" necessary to end a betrothal agreement.

9

What About 1 Corinthians 7?

Aside from Jesus' teaching in the Gospels, the Apostle Paul is the only other New Testament author who deals directly with the issue of divorce and remarriage. Furthermore, other than a brief (though important) comment in Romans 7:2-3, only one chapter in Paul's writing contains extensive teaching on these topics. That chapter is 1 Corinthians 7.

As we said earlier, no substantive argument can be made from 1 Corinthians 7 to justify a permissive stance toward divorce. Paul's prohibition of divorce is in perfect and obvious agreement with the teaching of Christ. When the question of divorce is addressed, he responds as follows:

> The wife should not leave her husband. (v. 10)

> The husband should not divorce his wife. (v. 11)

> If any brother has a wife who is an unbeliever, and she consents to live with him, he must not divorce her. (v. 12)

> A woman who has an unbelieving husband, and he consents to live with her, she must not send her husband away. (v. 13)

Four times in this chapter, Paul says, in effect, "Do not divorce your spouse." The closest he comes to even tolerating divorce is in verse 15 where the believing spouse is permitted to cooperate in a divorce if the unbelieving spouse insists on leaving. Paul gives no support for the idea that in certain cases it is acceptable for a person to initiate a divorce.

The controversy that stems from 1 Corinthians 7 primarily concerns the question of remarriage. Three verses in this chapter (vv. 9, 15, and 28) are commonly thought to support the idea that remarriage after divorce, even while a former spouse is living, is permitted in certain cases. The following chapters contain explanations of how we believe these three controversial verses are commonly misinterpreted.

It is important for the reader to understand that Paul changes topics several times in 1 Corinthians 7. He was replying to a letter from the Corinthian church. This chapter was his response "concerning the things [note the plural] about which you wrote" (7:1). These "things" were various questions related to marriage, divorce, and remarriage. It naturally follows that Paul's response would be in the form of separate and distinct answers. If these well-marked changes in subject matter are overlooked when interpreting the various parts of this chapter, it is easy to forget that Paul has switched from one topic to another. Failure to note these divisions could cause the reader to interpret Paul's words as if he were still addressing one of his former topics.

Paul's response to the Corinthians' concerns regarding marriage, divorce, and remarriage may be divided into seven basic sections. The following text of 1 Corinthians 7 is sectioned in order to show more clearly which categories of people Paul was addressing in the various parts of the chapter. We suggest that you read the entire text of 1 Corinthians 7 now, noting the divisions in topic, and then refer back to these pages when reading chapters 10-12.

The Complete Text of 1 Corinthians 7

Verses 1-7: Instructions regarding sexual relations in marriage

(1) Now concerning the things about which you wrote, it is good for a man not to touch a woman. (2) But because of immoralities, each man is to have his own wife, and each woman is to have her own husband. (3) The husband must fulfill his duty to his wife, and likewise also the wife to her husband. (4) The wife does not have authority over her own body, but the husband does; and likewise also the husband does not have authority over his own body, but the wife does. (5) Stop depriving one another, except by agreement for a

time, so that you may devote yourselves to prayer, and come together again so that Satan will not tempt you because of your lack of self-control. (6) But this I say by way of concession, not of command. (7) Yet I wish that all men were even as I myself am. However, each man has his own gift from God, one in this manner, and another in that.

Verses 8-9: Instructions to the unmarried and widows

(8) But I say to the unmarried and to widows that it is good for them if they remain even as I. (9) But if they do not have self-control, let them marry; for it is better to marry than to burn with passion.

Verses 10-11: Instructions to married believers

(10) But to the married I give instructions, not I, but the Lord, that the wife should not leave her husband (11) (but if she does leave, she must remain unmarried, or else be reconciled to her husband), and that the husband should not divorce his wife.

Verses 12-16: Instructions to believers married to unbelievers

(12) But to the rest I say, not the Lord, that if any brother has a wife who is an unbeliever, and she consents to live with him, he must not divorce her. (13) And a woman who has an unbelieving husband, and he consents to live with her, she must not send her husband away. (14) For the unbelieving husband is sanctified through his wife, and the unbelieving wife is sanctified through her believing husband; for otherwise your children are unclean, but now they are holy. (15) Yet if the unbelieving one leaves, let him leave; the brother or the sister is not under bondage in such cases, but God has called us to peace. (16) For how do you know, O wife, whether you will save your husband? Or how do you know, O husband, whether you will save your wife?

Verses 17-24: Instructions concerning contentment

(17) Only, as the Lord has assigned to each one, as God has called each, in this manner let him walk. And so I direct in all the churches. (18) Was any man called when he was already circumcised? He is not to become uncircumcised. Has anyone

been called in uncircumcision? He is not to be circumcised. (19) Circumcision is nothing, and uncircumcision is nothing, but what matters is the keeping of the commandments of God. (20) Each man must remain in that condition in which he was called. (21) Were you called while a slave? Do not worry about it; but if you are able also to become free, rather do that. (22) For he who was called in the Lord while a slave, is the Lord's freedman; likewise he who was called while free, is Christ's slave. (23) You were bought with a price; do not become slaves of men. (24) Brethren, each one is to remain with God in that condition in which he was called.

Verses 25-38: Instructions to those who have never been married

(25) Now concerning virgins I have no command of the Lord, but I give an opinion as one who by the mercy of the Lord is trustworthy. (26) I think then that this is good in view of the present distress, that it is good for a man to remain as he is. (27) Are you bound to a wife? Do not seek to be released. Are you released from a wife? Do not seek a wife. (28) But if you marry, you have not sinned; and if a virgin marries, she has not sinned. Yet such will have trouble in this life, and I am trying to spare you. (29) But this I say, brethren, the time has been shortened, so that from now on those who have wives should be as though they had none; (30) and those who weep, as though they did not weep; and those who rejoice, as though they did not rejoice; and those who buy, as though they did not possess; (31) and those who use the world, as though they did not make full use of it; for the form of this world is passing away.

(32) But I want you to be free from concern. One who is unmarried is concerned about the things of the Lord, how he may please the Lord; (33) but one who is married is concerned about the things of the world, how he may please his wife, (34) and his interests are divided. The woman who is unmarried, and the virgin, is concerned about the things of the Lord, that she may be holy both in body and spirit; but one who is married is concerned about the things of the world, how she may please her husband. (35) This I say for your own benefit; not to put a restraint upon you, but to promote what is appropriate and to secure undistracted devotion to the Lord.

(36) But if any man thinks that he is acting unbecomingly toward his virgin daughter, if she is past her youth, and if it must be so, let him do what he wishes, he does not sin; let her marry. (37) But he who stands firm in his heart, being under no constraint, but has authority over his own will, and has decided this in his own heart, to keep his own virgin daughter, he will do well. (38) So then both he who gives his own virgin daughter in marriage does well, and he who does not give her in marriage will do better.

Verses 39-40: Instructions to believing wives concerning remarriage

(39) A wife is bound as long as her husband lives; but if her husband is dead, she is free to be married to whom she wishes, only in the Lord. (40) But in my opinion she is happier if she remains as she is; and I think that I also have the Spirit of God.

Having noted the various subject changes in 1 Corinthians 7, we are prepared to examine verses 9, 15, and 28. We will do this in the next three chapters by quoting the biblical text of the passage in question, offering our own interpretive restatement of the passage, and explaining how we arrived at our conclusions.

10

Liberty for the Unmarried: Considering 1 Corinthians 7:8-9

The Biblical Text

(8) But I say to the unmarried and to widows that it is good for them if they remain even as I. (9) But if they do not have self-control, let them marry; for it is better to marry than to burn with passion.

Our Interpretive Restatement of Verses 8 and 9

But I say to widowers and widows that singleness is good if one has been given the gift of contented celibacy. But if one has not been given this gift—if a person is consumed with sexual passion and not truly content to remain single—then let that person marry. Singleness after the death of a spouse has its benefits, but it is not preferable if tainted by habitual sexual lust. It is better for widows and widowers to marry than to burn with sexual passion.

Justification of our Interpretive Restatement

One crucial question in this passage is, "Who are 'the unmarried'?" Is Paul addressing *all* who are not currently married, including divorced people? Or is he using the term "unmarried" in a more limited sense? We believe the term "unmarried" in verse 8 is most likely a reference to formerly married *men* whose wives had died (in other words, widowers). There is a specific Greek word for "widower," but it is never used in the New Testament, and there is no record of it being used in other Greek literature during the *Koine* period (i.e., the historical time span during which the common Greek of the New Testament was in use). Furthermore, there is reason to believe that the more general Greek word for "unmarried" (*agamos*) was sometimes used elsewhere to refer specifically to widowers.[29]

Also consider the following:

- ***Paul would not have included widows twice in the same verse.*** If the word "unmarried" in verse 8 ("But I say to the unmarried and to widows") were intended as a general term to refer to *all* who are not currently married (as is sometimes argued), Paul would have had no reason to list "widows" as a separate category in the same verse. Widows would fall into the general category of "the unmarried" (if it were intended to have such a general meaning here) just as would bachelors, virgins, divorced people, and widowers.

- ***Paul forbids remarriage after divorce two verses later.*** It is impossible to reconcile the opinion that Paul permitted a divorced person to remarry in verse 9, with the fact that he forbade the divorced woman to remarry in verse 11. People in that category are instructed to "remain unmarried, or else be reconciled to" their former spouse (v. 11).

Since Paul uses the word "unmarried" in verse 8 in a way that rules out widows and divorced people, and since he addresses those who have never been married later in the chapter (vv. 25ff), widowers are the only category of "unmarried" person remaining. Therefore this section must be addressed to widowers (i.e., "the unmarried") and widows.

If the above limitation of the meaning of the word "unmarried" is missed, one might conclude that Paul was providing a way out of temptation, through marriage, for a single person (even a divorced person) who was falling repeatedly into sexual sin. However, given Paul's prohibition of remarriage after divorce in verse 11, which reflects Jesus' teaching that remarriage after divorce is adultery, this would require us to believe that in verse 9 Paul was giving a *sinful*

---

29 See Gordon Fee, *The First Epistle to the Corinthians*, in the New International Commentary on the New Testament (Grand Rapids: Eerdmans Publishing Co., 1987), 287-288.

way of escape from a *sinful* pattern of behavior. Just three chapters later he tells us that "God is faithful, who will not allow you to be tempted beyond what you are able, but with the temptation will provide the way of escape also, so that you will be able to endure it" (10:13). In our view, the notion that God might provide one sin as the "way of escape" from another sin is unacceptable.

Paul permitted remarriage for widowers (i.e., "the unmarried") and widows in verse 9 for two reasons: First, remarriage is lawful for those whose spouses have died (1 Cor. 7:39; Rom. 7:3). Second, Paul did not want his personal preference for singleness to become a stumbling block to those in this category who had opted for singleness but were being overcome by the temptation to commit sexual sin. He was simply acknowledging that people whose spouses have died have the option of marrying if singleness proves too difficult. He may have still had in mind the fact that some of the Corinthian Christians had shown a propensity for following after one noteworthy teacher/apostle or another (i.e., Paul, Cephas, or Apollos; cf. 1:12). Excessive loyalty to Paul could have caused a widow or widower to think, "As a follower of Paul, I should remain single like Paul no matter what." Paul's response, in essence, was this: "Remaining single like me is good, but singleness is not better if you are struggling with sexual lust. If that is your situation, since you are permitted to marry and have not been given the gift of celibacy, then marriage is the better option."

We are aware that in verse 11 Paul describes the woman who has divorced her husband as being "unmarried," using the same word as in verse 8. This factor often causes interpreters to conclude that every other use of "unmarried" in chapter 7 (vv. 8, 32, and 34) must also include divorced people. But this generalization is both unnecessary and unwarranted. The word "unmarried" (*agamos*) describes people in three different situations: widowed, divorced, or never married. Interpreters of 1 Corinthians 7 must allow the meaning of this word to be variably restricted or broadened as the frequently changing context dictates. Verses 8 and 11 appear in two different sections of this chapter. In these two sections, two totally different topics are being addressed. Therefore interpreters are not obligated to expect the word to carry the same meaning in both places.

In summary, consider our interpretive restatement of verses 8-9 again:

> But I say to widowers and widows that singleness is good if one has been given the gift of contented celibacy. But if one has not been given this gift—if a person is consumed with sexual passion and not truly content to remain single—then let that person marry. Singleness after the death of a spouse has its benefits, but it is not preferable if tainted by habitual sexual lust. It is better for widows and widowers to marry than to burn with sexual passion.

11

Not Under Bondage:
Considering 1 Corinthians 7:12-16

The Biblical Text

> (12) But to the rest I say, not the Lord, that if any brother has a wife who is an unbeliever, and she consents to live with him, he must not divorce her. (13) And a woman who has an unbelieving husband, and he consents to live with her, she must not send her husband away. (14) For the unbelieving husband is sanctified through his wife, and the unbelieving wife is sanctified through her believing husband; for otherwise your children are unclean, but now they are holy. (15) Yet if the unbelieving one leaves, let him leave; the brother or the sister is not under bondage in such cases, but God has called us to peace. (16) For how do you know, O wife, whether you will save your husband? Or how do you know, O husband, whether you will save your wife?

Our Interpretive Restatement of Verses 12-16

> To Christians who are married to unbelievers, I say (and I am giving my own opinion here, not repeating something Jesus said), that if a Christian man has an unconverted wife who wants the marriage to continue, he must not divorce her. And if a Christian woman has an unconverted husband who wants the marriage to continue, she must not divorce him. I say this because the unconverted husband gains a spiritual advantage by living with his Christian wife, and the unconverted wife gains a spiritual advantage by living with her Christian husband. The presence of one believing spouse in a mixed

marriage even serves as a spiritual benefit to the children.[30] Nevertheless, if the unconverted spouse insists on a divorce, the Christian spouse is free to cooperate in the process. As long as the divorce is sought by, and initiated by, the unbeliever, the Christian spouse is not enslaved to my former command forbidding divorce. After all, God has called us to be peaceful, not to strive contentiously with unbelievers in order to preserve a disharmonious marriage. How do you know that peaceful cooperation with your spouse's decision to divorce won't bring about his or her conversion?[31]

Justification of Our Interpretive Restatement

It is commonly taught that the phrase "not under bondage" in verse 15 means that the believer who has been divorced by a disobedient spouse is no longer bound to the former spouse in a one-flesh union, and is therefore free to remarry. In our view this cannot be the correct interpretation. We believe that when Paul said "not under bondage," he was simply releasing the believing spouse from the obligation to cling to the marriage when the unbeliever wants to leave. Consider the following arguments for this conclusion:

- *Paul uses a word that is never used elsewhere to describe being bound in marriage.* The word Paul uses for "under bondage" in verse 15 (*douloō*) is not the same word he uses everywhere else to denote the obligation related to marriage or betrothal. He consistently uses the word *deō* for this purpose (1 Cor. 7:27, 39; Rom. 7:2). Furthermore, Paul's pattern is to use *douloō* to describe a person being (or becoming) enslaved (Rom. 6:18, 22; 1 Cor. 9:19; Gal. 4:3; Titus 2:3). Aside from the debated meaning of *douloō* in 1 Corinthians 7:15, the word is never used elsewhere

---

30 The statement about children is controversial. We have offered one possible meaning, but would not want to contend vigorously for our interpretive restatement of this particular phrase. The meaning of this phrase does not greatly affect the overall understanding of the passage concerning our subject.

31 Our interpretation of verse 16 assumes that Paul was encouraging the Corinthians by saying that cooperation in such a divorce would more likely result in the conversion of the unbelieving spouse. Other interpreters believe Paul was saying, "The conversion of your unbelieving spouse is not a certain prospect, so don't cling contentiously to the marriage for the sake of saving him or her." The difference between these two interpretations is subtle, and they are not totally at odds with each other. One simply assumes a more encouraging tone, and the other a more skeptical tone.

in the New Testament to refer to the marriage bond. Therefore, when Paul says the abandoned believer is "not under bondage," using *douloō* instead of *deō*, the interpreter's first inclination should be to conclude that Paul is describing something other than the obligation related to marriage or betrothal.

- **Paul's flow of thought indicates that divorce, not remarriage, was the issue.** The context, both before and after the statement in verse 15, works against the conclusion that Paul permitted remarriage after divorce when he said, "the brother or the sister is not under bondage in such cases." Consider the logical flow of thought in these verses:

1. First Paul instructs believers not to divorce their unbelieving spouses (vv. 12-13).

2. Next he explains that remaining married to an unbeliever helps the unbeliever (v. 14a). Even the children of such a union experience some benefit (v. 14b).

3. He then frees the believing spouse from strict observance of the "no-divorce" requirement in the event that the unbeliever insists on a divorce (v. 15a). The believer is "not under bondage" to Paul's prohibition of divorce "in such cases."

4. Finally he explains why cooperation in a divorce is allowable "in such cases." "God has called us to peace" (v. 15b-16), meaning that cooperation "in such cases" is better than contentiously striving to preserve the marriage in the hope that the unbeliever will be converted.[32]

---

32 We do not believe Paul was saying that a believing spouse should never resist being divorced by an unbeliever. Marriage is precious in God's sight and should be preserved whenever possible. This will often mean reasoning, even pleading, with an unconverted spouse who expresses the desire to divorce. These efforts are perfectly appropriate, even mandatory, before giving in to the unbeliever's desire. Once the efforts to preserve the marriage have been proven fruitless, however, the believer's dignified cooperation in the process is not only permitted, but is actually better than contentiously striving to prevent the inevitable.

Paul answers one question in verses 12-16, and one question only: "Must a Christian remain married to an unbelieving spouse?" His answer (paraphrased) is, "Yes, unless the unbelieving spouse insists on ending the marriage. In such cases, the believer is not enslaved to the general prohibition of divorce, but is permitted to cooperate for the sake of peace." Paul's answer informs the believer that avoiding divorce "in such cases" is not absolutely necessary, but his answer never approaches the subject of remarriage after divorce. Aside from the meaning many interpreters automatically assign to the English phrase "under bondage" or "bound" (which, as we will explain below, are not the best translations of *douloō*), nothing in the context indicates that Paul was permitting remarriage after an unwanted divorce. It seems that it is only when interpreters assume that the Bible provides such permissiveness (perhaps on the basis of their understanding of Matthew 19:9) that this statement appears to provide it.

- *The same exact situation is addressed conclusively in the Gospels.* Matthew 5:32 and Luke 16:18 prohibit remarriage after divorce in the same type of situation as described in 1 Corinthians 7:15—when one spouse has been sinfully abandoned (divorced) by another. In both of these examples, remarriage for the abandoned spouse is said to constitute adultery.

- *Paul prohibits remarriage after divorce elsewhere.* Paul cannot be contradicting his own teaching earlier in the same chapter (v. 11), and his own statement in Romans 7:3a ("So then, if while her husband is living she is joined to another man, she shall be called an adulteress.").

In summary, consider our interpretive restatement of verses 12-16 once again.

To Christians who are married to unbelievers, I say (and I am giving my own opinion here, not repeating something Jesus said), that if a Christian man has an unconverted wife who wants the marriage to continue, he must not divorce her. And if a Christian woman has an unconverted husband who wants the marriage to continue, she must not divorce him. I say this because the unconverted husband gains a spiritual advantage by living with his Christian wife, and the unconverted wife gains a spiritual advantage by living with her Christian husband. The presence of one believing spouse in a mixed marriage even serves as a spiritual benefit to the children. Nevertheless, if the unconverted spouse insists on a divorce, the Christian spouse is free to cooperate in the process. As long as the divorce is sought by, and initiated by, the unbeliever, the Christian spouse is not enslaved to my former command forbidding divorce. After all, God has called us to be peaceful, not to strive contentiously with unbelievers in order to preserve a disharmonious marriage. How do you know that peaceful cooperation with your spouse's decision to divorce won't bring about his or her conversion?

12

Bound and Released: Considering 1 Corinthians 7:25-28

The Biblical Text

> (25) Now concerning virgins I have no command of the Lord, but I give an opinion as one who by the mercy of the Lord is trustworthy. (26) I think then that this is good in view of the present distress, that it is good for a man to remain as he is. (27a) Are you bound to a wife? Do not seek to be released. (27b) Are you released from a wife? Do not seek a wife. (28a) But if you marry, you have not sinned; (28b) and if a virgin marries, she has not sinned. Yet such will have trouble in this life, and I am trying to spare you.

Our Interpretive Restatement of Verses 25-28

> Now, concerning the issue of those who are betrothed, I have no direct instructions from the Lord, but I give my own opinion as one who by the mercy of the Lord is trustworthy. I think it is best, in view of the well-known difficulties we now face as Christians, that a man be content to remain in whatever situation he finds himself with respect to marital obligations and commitments. Are you a never-married man who is bound to a woman in a betrothal relationship? Then remain as you are. Do not seek to be excused from the obligations of your betrothal. On the other hand, are you a never-married man who is free from any betrothal obligation to a woman? Then be satisfied with your singleness and do not seek to find a woman to whom you may become bound. But I do not say this in order to forbid you to marry. If you, as a never-married man, decide to marry, you have not sinned. And if a never-

married woman decides to marry, she has not sinned. Yet if you do marry, you will experience increased difficulty in this life, and I would like to see you spared from difficulty as much as possible.

Justification of Our Interpretive Restatement

Verses 27-28 are commonly (but we believe, wrongly) interpreted as permitting remarriage for a divorced person. Though we disagree, this interpretation is certainly understandable. The word "released" in 27a and the phrase "released from a wife" in 27b *seem* to imply a marriage being ended by divorce. When 28a follows by giving permission for the person who is "released from a wife" to marry, it is easy to see why many interpreters take it as permission for a divorced person to remarry. Nevertheless, this seemingly obvious interpretation fails to account for several important factors.

- *In verse 25 Paul introduces a new topic.* He says "Now concerning virgins . . . ." This introduction serves to inform the reader that Paul is no longer addressing the question of divorce, which he covered in verses 10-16, but rather the situation of betrothal.[33] Paul's betrothal-specific language dominates from verse 25 through verse 38. To interpret 28a as giving a divorced person permission to remarry is to completely overlook this distinct change in context.

- *Interpreters should not see a command from Christ where Paul says none is given.* In verse 25 Paul says, "Now concerning virgins *I have no command of the Lord*, but *I give an opinion* as one who by the mercy of the Lord is trustworthy" (emphasis added). Paul's "opinion" is then explained in verse 26 where he tells the reader that "it is good for a man to remain as he is." In verse 27 Paul follows this introduction by giving two examples of the way this principle should be carried out in practice.

---

33 See the ESV and NET where this is made clear in translation. The ESV says, "Now concerning the betrothed," and the NET reads, "With regard to the question about people who have never married."

Example 1 (27a):
"Are you bound to a wife? Do not seek to be released."

Example 2 (27b):
"Are you released from a wife? Do not seek a wife."

If the first example (27a) is addressed to the married man, it is difficult to see how it could logically follow Paul's introductory statement that he has "no command of the Lord." If the words, "Do not seek to be released," are a command not to divorce (as many interpreters insist), then it most certainly *is* a command from the Lord. As Jesus said, "What therefore God has joined together, let no man separate" (Matt. 19:6; Mark 10:9). Paul himself paraphrased this prohibition *as being a command from Christ* earlier in the same chapter (vv. 10-11). The logical conclusion is that since Paul prefaces this section by explicitly stating that he is *not* repeating any command from Christ in his address to virgins, then he is *not* addressing the married man in 27a. He is addressing the never-married man who is betrothed.

- *Interpreters should allow the context to be the final determiner of the meaning of a word.* The Greek word for "wife" (*gunē*) is the same as the word for "woman," and the term "bound" (*deō*) could apply to a betrothal obligation as well as to a consummated marriage (as in 1 Corinthians 7:39 and Romans 7:3 where marriage is obviously in view). Given the context in which this statement is made, Paul must have been addressing the betrothed man. His question could be stated like this: "Are you, *the never-married man*, bound to a *woman* in a betrothal relationship." This fits the context much better than, "Are you, *the married man*, bound to a *wife* in a consummated marriage."[34]

- *Paul gives a clear reminder in verse 28 that he is addressing the subject of betrothal, not divorce and remarriage.* By extending the permission to marry in 28b

---

34 Even if one were to insist that modern translations correctly use "wife" and not "woman" in verse 27, the only "wife" supported by the context is one who is betrothed to a "husband," like Mary was to Joseph.

only to women who are *virgins* and not to women who are divorced or widowed, Paul reminds the reader that the current block of instruction is intended for the never-married (or betrothed). In other words, he finally addresses *female* virgins in 28b. Everything up to this point (vv. 25-28a) was directed to *male* virgins.

- **Paul would not have given instructions that had no relevance to the subject at hand.** The permission to marry given in 28a is clearly addressed to the same man who is "released from a wife" in 27b. Therefore, if "released from a wife" in 27b *must* mean "divorced" (as some interpreters insist[35]), then the permission given in 28a—"But if you marry, you have not sinned"—has no application whatsoever for the man who has never been married. The never-married man *cannot* be "released from a wife" if "released from a wife" means "divorced." But verses 27 and 28 are Paul's key instruction in a passage introduced by the words, "Now concerning virgins," and concluded by the betrothal-specific language of verses 36-38. We find it unreasonable to interpret Paul's key instruction in this passage in a way that has no bearing whatsoever on the principal subject he is addressing.

- **The Greek word Paul uses for "released from" (luō) in verse 27 does not necessarily imply a former marital union.** Even though the word *luō* can technically mean "released after being bound" with reference to a marital relationship, it is never known to have been used this way in Koine Greek, whether speaking of biblical or extra-biblical writing. As Gordon Fee notes, the word is "otherwise unknown to denote divorce."[36] In its most basic definition, *luō* is simply a direct opposite of *deō* (the word for "bound" in 27a). In this context, where Paul is clearly addressing virgins (i.e., the betrothed) it would be more safely translated in 27b as "not bound to" rather than "released from." As an imperfect but helpful illustration

---

35 For example, see Jay Adams, *Marriage, Divorce, and Remarriage in the Bible* (Grand Rapids: Baker Books, 1980), 84.

36 Fee, *The First Epistle to the Corinthians*, 331.

of the way we believe *deō* and *luō* stand in relation to one another in this context, think of the condition of the shoelaces when you take a new pair of shoes out of their box. You would rightly say that they are "untied" (*luō*) even though they have never been "tied" (*deō*).

- ***"Do not seek to be released" carries a different meaning than "Do not divorce."*** The phrase, "Do not *seek to be* released" (27a, emphasis added) seems to imply that the condition of actually *being* released is not immediately or automatically available to the person Paul is addressing. It is a change of status that must be sought after. This fits the situation of a betrothal arrangement quite nicely, where the betrothed man would need to seek the cooperation of the virgin's father (and/or the virgin herself) in order to be excused from his obligation. It also better explains Paul's choice of the word *luō* which, though never used in biblical or extra-biblical literature to refer to divorce, "is found throughout the papyri as a technical term for discharging someone from the obligations of a contract."[37] The command, "do not seek to be released," on the other hand, does not fit well at all with the typical New Testament commands related to divorce. Believers are never told not to "seek to be" divorced. Jesus and Paul simply say (in essence) "Do not divorce" (Matt. 19:6; Mark 10:9; 1 Cor. 7:10, 11, 12, 13). The person being addressed in the "do not divorce" passages has sole discretion either to divorce or not to divorce, as well as the immediate capability of divorcing if he or she so chooses.

- ***Paul would not contradict himself.*** As we previously stated concerning verses 9 and 15, verse 28 cannot be rightly taken as a contradiction of verses 10-11 where Paul prohibits remarriage after divorce.

---

37 Ibid.

In summary, consider our interpretive restatement of verses 25-28 again:

> Now, concerning the issue of those who are betrothed, I have no direct instructions from the Lord, but I give my own opinion as one who by the mercy of the Lord is trustworthy. I think it is best, in view of the well-known difficulties we now face as Christians, that a man be content to remain in whatever situation he finds himself with respect to marital obligations and commitments. Are you a never-married man who is bound to a woman in a betrothal relationship? Then remain as you are. Do not seek to be excused from the obligations of your betrothal. On the other hand, are you a never-married man who is free from any betrothal obligation to a woman? Then be satisfied with your singleness and do not seek to find a woman to whom you may become bound. But I do not say this in order to forbid you to marry. If you, as a never-married man, decide to marry, you have not sinned. And if a never-married woman decides to marry, she has not sinned. Yet if you do marry, you will experience increased difficulty in this life, and I would like to see you spared from difficulty as much as possible.

13

A Brief Evaluation of the Current Consensus

Our purpose in writing this book was not primarily to examine and critique other views. We were mainly concerned with explaining our own position and its practical implications. We realize, however, that many, if not most, who read our work have been taught that divorce and remarriage are permissible in cases of adultery. Because this view has prevailed among evangelicals since the Protestant Reformation, and because it is currently endorsed by many reputable Bible teachers, those who have read Part 1 of our book may be struggling at this point to decide which position is biblical and which is in error. We do not wish to distract readers away from our main purpose by engaging in a lengthy critical argument, but we believe it will be helpful at this point to demonstrate briefly that the prevailing view has significant weaknesses.

As we explained in chapter 5, the common opinion that divorce and remarriage are permitted in cases of adultery is based largely, if not entirely, on Matthew 19:9. Despite Jesus' categorical prohibition of divorce in Matthew 19:6 and Mark 10:9, and despite His repeated declarations that remarriage after divorce is adultery (Matt. 5:32; Mark 10:11-12; Luke 16:18), the permissive interpretation of Matthew 19:9 is often given the greatest interpretive weight. Texts that contain no exceptions are then interpreted as though they did—as though the permissiveness thought to be represented in Matthew 19:9 were so universally understood by first century readers that the other New Testament authors saw no need to put it in writing. Even the permissive interpretations of 1 Corinthians

7 ultimately trace their justification back to this single verse in Matthew's Gospel. In our view (as we explained in chapter 5) the interpretive priority given to Matthew 19:9 is unjustifiable, especially since it is the most ambiguous of all the biblical texts related to divorce and remarriage. It would take a book larger than this one to critique all of the rational, textual, and historical factors that lead interpreters to adopt the permissive view, and other published works already exist to serve that purpose.[38] Therefore, we will focus in this chapter on just one widely accepted theory as to why divorce and remarriage are permitted in cases of adultery.

Perhaps the most popular contemporary explanation of the rationale behind the opinion that divorce and remarriage are permitted in cases of adultery stems from the Old Testament law requiring the death penalty for adultery (Lev. 20:10; Deut. 22:22). By bringing about the death of the guilty spouse, the Old Testament law resulted in freedom for the innocent spouse to remarry. Proponents of the view we will consider in this chapter assert that because God graciously abrogated the death penalty for adultery under the administration of the new covenant (and/or because the Jews were no longer enforcing the death penalty for adultery), Jesus permitted divorce and remarriage in order to permanently preserve the same freedom for the innocent spouse. One well-respected advocate of this position argues as follows:

> If God is gracious to the sinning spouse by tolerating divorce instead of requiring execution, He would surely also be gracious to the innocent spouse by permitting remarriage, which was permissible when a spouse died (cf. Rom. 7:2-3). The purpose of permitting divorce is to show mercy to the sinning spouse, not to condemn the innocent one to a lifetime of singleness and loneliness that would not be required if the Lord had the sinning partner executed. Should His grace to the sinner penalize the innocent? The Lord allows divorce in order that the adulterer might have the opportunity to repent rather than be put to death. Both here [Matthew 19:9] and in Matthew 5:32 Jesus specifically allows remarriage by the

---

38 For example, see William A. Heth and Gordon J. Wenham, *Jesus and Divorce: The Problem with the Evangelical Consensus* (Nashville: Thomas Nelson Publishers, 1985).

innocent spouse in order that he or she might have opportunity to enjoy again the blessings of marriage that were destroyed by the other spouse's adultery.[39]

While it may seem fair and logical for God to permit divorce and remarriage for the innocent spouse in the absence of the death penalty, this popular conclusion has the following weaknesses:

- First, if Jesus' intent in giving the exception clause were to preserve the freedom to remarry that was provided by Old Testament death penalty laws, it stands to reason that He would have sought to preserve this freedom for every type of Old Testament death penalty offense, not just adultery.

  Death was prescribed for a vast range of sins in the Law of Moses, from adultery (Lev. 20:10), to murder (Ex. 21:12; Deut. 19:11-13), to striking or cursing a parent (Ex. 21:15, 17), to kidnapping (Ex. 21:16), to sorcery (Ex. 22:18), to encouraging idolatry (Deut. 13:1-11), to the practice of idolatry (Deut. 17:2-5), to refusing to act in accordance with the determinations of a Levitical judge (Deut. 17:12), to uttering false prophecies in the name of the true God or prophesying in the name of a false God (Deut. 18:20), to being a false witness in a capital murder case (Deut. 19:16-21), to rape (Deut. 22:25). The spouse of a person who was executed for any of these crimes was freed to remarry.

  Under the new covenant, the death penalty is no longer required for most of these offenses. Therefore we would ask, "Should a godly 21st century wife whose husband worships idols, or a godly 21st century husband whose wife practices sorcery, be compelled to remain married when he or she would have been freed from the offending spouse through the death penalty under the old covenant? Should not these 'innocent spouses' be permitted to divorce and remarry?" As the writer quoted above asks, "Should His grace to the sinner penalize the innocent?" The truth is, unless *every* sin that required the death penalty under the old covenant

39 MacArthur, *The MacArthur New Testament Commentary: Matthew 16-23*, 171.

now justifies divorce and remarriage (which no sound interpreter alleges as far as we know), the same logic that leads interpreters to adopt the popular position also serves to disprove it.

- Second, the position relies upon assumptions and conjecture but lacks solid textual support. This is evident from the first sentence of the above quote, where God's presumed graciousness toward the guilty spouse in permitting divorce instead of death leads to the assumption that He also graciously permits remarriage for the innocent spouse. The writer concludes by stating, as though it were unarguable, not only *that* Jesus permits remarriage for the innocent spouse, but also *why* He permits it.

  As we have shown in Part 1 of this book, there is no text of Scripture that conclusively proves that God permits divorce in cases of adultery, while several passages prohibit divorce categorically. Even if God does permit divorce in cases of adultery, nothing in Scripture indicates that He does so "instead of requiring execution," or "to show mercy to the sinning spouse," or "in order that the adulterer might have opportunity to repent rather than be put to death." These conclusions about God's motives stem from speculation alone. Furthermore, even if such speculations about God's reasons for permitting divorce were correct, nothing is *written* about His reasons that would justify the above-quoted author's conclusions regarding remarriage. Matthew 19:9 is, at best, inconclusive on the subject of remarriage after divorce, and in Matthew 5:32 Jesus clearly prohibits remarriage after divorce, even for the innocent spouse, by specifying that though she was not guilty of adultery prior to the divorce, she commits adultery when she remarries.

In the final analysis, while the popular position described above may *seem* fair and logical, it is balanced precariously on a foundation of assumptions and cemented together with human reason, having no conclusive support from even a single biblical text. In our view this is no way to formulate an opinion on a critical issue like divorce and remarriage, especially when there are exegetically sound reasons for arriving at a competing view.

Part 2

Applying What We Have Learned

Introduction to Part 2

The way we answer questions and give counsel about marriage, divorce, and remarriage depends on what we believe the Bible teaches concerning these subjects. Before reading what follows, therefore, we hope you will become familiar with our doctrinal conclusions as explained and defended in the preceding pages. As a reminder to those who have already read Part 1, we believe the Bible's teaching on marriage, divorce, and remarriage can be summarized in three assertions:

- The one-flesh union created in marriage is permanent until death.

- Initiating a divorce is never lawful.

- Remarrying after divorce is an act of adultery if a former spouse is living.

We do not believe that the integrity of the Scriptures concerning this difficult and sensitive topic can be preserved without arriving at these conclusions. As we have already noted, we refer to our position as the "permanence" view.

14

A Note to Those Who Disagree

For those who have read Part 1 but continue to believe that divorce and/or remarriage are permitted biblically in certain situations, the permanence view may seem not only incorrect, but also without compassion. It may appear that we are saying to people in miserable marriages or situations of unwanted singleness, "That's just the way it is in God's kingdom, so you had better learn to deal with your misery." Far from this being our attitude, we recognize the great hardship people in these situations often experience. We think, for example, of the difficulties faced by the man whose wife is a habitual adulteress, or the woman whose husband is a violent alcoholic. We feel sorrow for the divorced single mother who struggles to provide for her children. For people with problems like these, divorce and/or remarriage might seem to represent true solutions. We believe these people (as well as those who counsel them) often overlook the disadvantages of divorcing and/or remarrying after divorce. Even if divorce and remarriage were lawful in God's eyes, consider these good reasons not to do either one:

- Even the most reputable advocates of the view that divorce is permitted in certain cases go to great lengths to discourage it. John Murray comments, for example, that divorce "could not be contemplated otherwise than as a radical breach of the divine institution."[40] Murray goes on to say, "Divorce is contrary to the divine institution, contrary to the nature of marriage, and contrary to the divine action

---

40 John Murray, *Divorce* (Phillipsburg: Presbyterian and Reformed Publishing Co., 1961), 1.

by which the union is effected."[41] John MacArthur, who shares Murray's opinion that divorce is permitted in cases of adultery, writes, "At best, divorce and remarriage is *only permitted* by the Lord, *never commended* and certainly never commanded, as some of Jesus' contemporary rabbis taught" (emphasis ours).[42]

- According to Patrick Fagan and Robert Rector, "Divorce seems to perpetuate itself across successive generations. The impact on home life is so strong that children of divorced parents struggle as adults to create a positive, healthy family environment for their own children. Adults who experienced divorce as children prove less capable of breaking the cycle and instead pass on a legacy of tragedy to their children and grandchildren. . . . One important difference between marriages that stay intact and those that end in divorce is the couple's ability to handle conflict and move toward agreement. Children of divorced parents can acquire the same incapacity to work through conflict from their parents."[43]

- Fagan and Rector go on to say that children whose parents have divorced "exhibit more health, behavioral, and emotional problems, are involved more frequently in crime and drug abuse, and have higher suicide rates." They also "more frequently demonstrate a diminished learning capacity, performing more poorly than their peers from intact two-parent families in reading, spelling, and math. They have higher dropout rates and lower rates of college graduation."[44]

- Divorce is financially unwise, generally resulting in a reduction of household income. "According to data

---

41 Ibid., 33.

42 MacArthur, *The MacArthur New Testament Commentary: Matthew 16-23*, 167.

43 Patrick Fagan and Robert Rector, "The Effects of Divorce on America," The World & I Online, October, 2000, http://www.worldandi.comspecialreport/divorce/divorce.html (accessed May 5, 2007). Patrick F. Fagan is William H.G. FitzGerald Senior Fellow in Family and Cultural Issues, and Robert Rector is Senior Research Fellow in Domestic Policy Studies, at the Heritage Foundation (www.heritage.org).

44 Ibid.

reported in 1994 by Mary Corcoran, professor of political science at the University of Michigan, 'During the years children lived with two parents, their family incomes averaged $43,600, and when these same children lived with one parent, their family incomes averaged $25,300.'[45] In addition to reducing household income, the divorce process itself is costly and leads to long-term expense obligations (such as travel costs related to visitation arrangements, additional childcare costs, etc.).

- Statistically, remarriage after divorce is a risky venture. As one writer notes, "A considerably larger number of second marriages end in divorce. John Haskey has analyzed the statistics for all those aged between 20 and 40 who married in England between 1951 and 1989 and who had divorced by 1995. The marriages of divorced men were 58% more likely to end in divorce than those of men who had never married before; for divorced women the figure was 81%. In the USA . . . 60-65% of remarriages after divorce end in a second divorce . . . . Although the total number of divorces has recently leveled off somewhat, the proportion of second divorces continues to increase."[46]

- Remarriage where children are involved creates complex step-relationships that are often problematic. For example, in a step-family, children are expected to submit to the parental authority of the new "mother" or "father," though this person is not their biological parent. Where the expectations and disciplinary standards differ greatly from those of the biological parent whom the step-parent has replaced, conflict is inevitable. Also, in a step-family the biological parent who retains custody of his or her children has a longer-term (and typically closer) bond with the children than with his or her new spouse. This could cause problems, for example, if the step-parent has a disciplinary conflict with a step-child. The biological parent's longstanding loyalty to the child might be pitted against the

---

45 Ibid.

46 Andrew Cornes, *Divorce and Remarriage: Biblical Principles and Pastoral Practice* (Ross-shire: Christian Focus Publications, 2002), 12.

new loyalty to the step-parent. It is not that step-relationships never prosper, but even under "ideal" conditions, the complex relational factors involved make them much more difficult to establish and maintain than natural-parent, intact-family relationships.

Divorce provides no guarantee of happiness. Rather than solving the problem of a difficult marriage, it further complicates life and confuses children. Marriages after divorce are sometimes thought to provide a sure solution to the problems related to divorce, but they more often result only in additional pain and hardship. Most importantly, the above would all be disadvantages of divorcing and/ or remarrying after divorce *even if divorce and remarriage were biblically lawful*. But as we have sought to demonstrate in Part 1, this is not the case.

15

Questions About Difficult Marital Situations

Every situation involving divorce and remarriage is unique and personal. There are untold numbers of variables and potential complications. We have not come close to addressing every possible situation in the following scenarios. The balance of this book is written to demonstrate how the permanence view affects the way we move forward in life, and/or the way we look back at past decisions and actions.

1. Adultery Followed by Repentance

Q: My husband and I are Christians, but he recently admitted that he has had an affair. He said the relationship with the other woman is over, and he begged me to forgive him. He said he wants to make things right, but I am so angry and hurt that I cannot imagine ever seeing him as my husband again. I want to divorce him. What should I do?

A: As impossible as this may seem at the moment, you should forgive your husband from your heart and seek to restore your relationship with him. There can be no minimizing of the pain you feel. Adultery is an awful offense, not only against God, but also against a husband or wife. Nevertheless, both Paul and Jesus disallowed divorce categorically, making no exception for sexual unfaithfulness in a consummated marriage. Furthermore, forgiveness is the standard to which Christians are called in the New Testament (Matt. 6:14-15; 18:21-35; Luke 17:3; Eph. 4:32; Col. 3:12-13). Because we have been granted repentance ourselves (Acts 11:18; 2 Tim. 2:25) and have been forgiven an immeasurable debt of sin, we have no right to withhold forgiveness from others, even when their sin against us is very great.

Reconciliation with your husband may take time, of course. There is no reason for you (or him) to presume that your life together should immediately return to normal just because of his admission of guilt, his apparent repentance, and your forgiveness. Trust is an essential component of reconciliation. Your forgiveness does not necessarily imply that your ability to trust your husband has been fully restored. If your husband is truly repentant, he will be willing to patiently rebuild your trust in him and thus bring about true and lasting reconciliation. As part of this process, he should be willing to submit to biblical counseling and become accountable to other men in your local church.

2. Ongoing Adultery Without Genuine Repentance

Q: My husband has been unfaithful to me on several occasions. He claims to be a Christian, and he seems genuinely remorseful after each incident, but he never truly repents of his unfaithfulness. I fear that as long as I stay married to him this will be an ongoing pattern. What should I do?

A: Our counsel to you would be the same as in the previous scenario. You should be prepared and willing to forgive your husband from your heart if he does repent, and you should continue to pursue his repentance and reconciliation with him. Take seriously what Jesus said about forgiving a person "seventy times seven" (Matt. 18:21-22). As difficult as this may seem, you should not divorce him.

There is more that needs to be said, however, about a situation where sexual unfaithfulness becomes habitual and does result in divorce. God is strong, but His people sometimes act out their weakness. It is possible that another person's habitual sin could drive even a mature Christian, in a time of weakness, to a sinful response like divorce. Jesus and Paul seemed to recognize that divorce might sometimes occur, even though both disallowed it. With this in mind, we will discuss later what should occur in the event that a Christian divorces a habitually immoral or abusive spouse (see scenario 21, "The Necessity of Church Discipline for Divorce and/or Remarriage," in chapter 18).

3. Pastoral Counsel in Cases of Habitual Adultery

Q: As a pastor, I am counseling a man whose wife has committed adultery multiple times, with multiple partners. She has often come to him with tears of sorrow, asking for forgiveness, and he has received her back. But she has always returned to her pattern of immorality. I agree that divorce is not a valid option, but what should I tell him to do?

A: In our view, your role as a pastor is to supply this person with comfort in his pain along with the biblical knowledge he needs to handle this situation in obedience to Christ. You should encourage him to patiently work toward reconciliation while remaining ready to forgive. You should tell him not to initiate a divorce under any circumstances.

You should also make him aware of the *advantages* of not divorcing as well as the *disadvantages* of terminating the marriage (as listed in chapter 14). For example, though his wife's married status has not restrained her from committing adultery, it *is* preventing her from entering into another marital union. If he were to divorce her, she would likely remarry, thus ending all realistic hope of the current marriage being restored. Since remarriage after divorce is not an option while a former spouse is living, her second marriage would end all biblical prospects of him ever again being married unless she were to die. But if he patiently (and obediently) refrains from divorcing her, the Lord may grant her true repentance and their marriage may be restored at some point in the future.

4. Pastoral Counsel in Other Seemingly Unbearable Situations

Q: I am a pastor faced with a marital counseling situation that does not involve sexual unfaithfulness. Rather, a violently abusive husband represents a serious threat to his wife. Does the permanence view require this woman to stay in the same home and sleep in the same bed with her husband, even though she is in great danger?

A: No, we would not say that. Where one spouse is faced with the serious risk of personal harm or harm to children in the home (e.g., because of the other spouse's alcohol or drug abuse, violent anger, criminal activity, sexual perversion, or even insanity), he or she may, if absolutely necessary, physically separate from the offending spouse while remaining open to the possibility of reconciliation.[47]

Some people may conclude that voluntary separation is never allowable because it violates the scriptural mandate for a spouse to render sexual affection to his or her husband or wife, as taught in 1 Corinthians 7:2-5. Paul's instruction in this passage, however, was designed to address a particular Corinthian error—sexual self-denial for misguided religious reasons. He was not saying that a woman whose husband represented a serious threat of bodily harm was to remain in the house with him no matter how great the danger. He simply wanted husbands and wives who were living together to continue having sexual relations in order to help each other resist sexual sin.

In cases where voluntary separation is deemed necessary because of extreme hardship or physical danger, pastors and counselors should show the utmost sympathy for the abused spouse and should do everything possible to assist in his or her protection.[48] Furthermore, local church bodies should go to great lengths to see that church members in these situations are supported spiritually, physically, emotionally, and even financially when necessary. As Paul says, we are to "do good to all people, and especially to those who are of the household of the faith" (Gal. 6:10).

5. Using Physical Separation as a Means to Induce Marital Reform

Q: My husband professes to be a Christian and we belong to the same church, but he behaves in many ways like an unbeliever. He drinks regularly to the point of drunkenness and stays out late with friends, sometimes most of the night. He has no apparent moral standard when it comes to movies or TV, and I have reason to

---

47 We are not advocating legal separation, which usually proves to be a precursor to divorce, but we would also not strictly prohibit legal separation, since it is never addressed in the Bible. There may be laws in some places that make legal separation necessary in order to obtain protective orders or financial support, but apart from these unavoidable contingencies, we believe it is unwise to take any legal step in the direction of divorce. We do believe, however, that some situations justify temporary (even if lengthy) physical separation for reasons of personal safety.

48 Pastors or counselors may be required by law to report the offending spouse's criminal behavior to law enforcement authorities in certain circumstances.

suspect that he is becoming emotionally (if not physically) involved with another woman. A Christian friend advised me to set certain "boundaries" in our marriage by telling my husband what is, and is not, acceptable behavior. She further said that if he fails to stay within these "boundaries," I should move out of the house with the children until he reforms his behavior. Should I heed my friend's counsel?

A: Your friend is right to say that you should tell your husband that his behavior is unacceptable. Every Christian has the biblical obligation to lovingly restrain other professing Christians from sinning (Matt. 18:15; Luke 17:3; James 5:19-20). But in our view, your friend's counsel about using the threat of separation as a means to prompt his reform is unbiblical and would likely prove counter-productive. Consider three reasons not to use the threat of separation (or actual separation) as a pressure tactic:

1. Sinful behavior in a professing Christian is to be dealt with through the local church if it cannot be resolved privately. Your friend has encouraged you to *begin* biblically by confronting your husband concerning his sin (Matt. 18:15), but her subsequent counsel about separation bypasses biblical instruction altogether. If your husband does not repent after you speak to him in private (Matt. 18:15), Christ would not have you move out of the house. He would have you address your husband in the presence of two or three others from the church (Matt. 18:16). If this did not bring true repentance, you (or more likely a pastor who is involved in the situation) should inform the whole church of the problem (Matt. 18:17). If your husband fails to respond even to public appeals for his repentance, the church should consider him an unbeliever and exclude him from their fellowship. This has not solved your problem altogether, but it has given you (and everyone else involved) a more accurate understanding of what the problem truly is. Furthermore, the Bible gives us reason to hope that the church's proper involvement may eventually prompt your husband to repent (1 Cor. 5:5).

2. Your friend's well-meaning counsel will likely backfire. Even though temporary separation is sometimes unavoidable (i.e., for reasons of personal safety), it rarely results in reconciliation. It more often increases momentum toward divorce, making the offending spouse's repentance *less* likely, not more. Separation removes the unbelieving (or professedly Christian) spouse from the sanctifying influence of the Christian home. The effect of this influence is precisely why Paul told Christians not to divorce their unbelieving spouses (1 Cor. 7:12-14). In 1 Peter 3:1-2, the counsel given to a wife with a disobedient husband looks hopefully toward the husband's repentance. Peter's hope of this positive outcome, however, is grounded on the fact that the disobedient husband will be living in the presence of his godly wife. He says such husbands may "be won without a word by the behavior of their wives, *as they observe your chaste and respectful behavior*" (emphasis added). This clearly implies living together despite the husband's disobedience.

3. Voluntary separation from a disobedient spouse for the sake of personal happiness is never condoned in Scripture. Your friend obviously wants you to be happy in your marriage. She hopes separation will cause your husband to end your suffering by reforming his behavior. The problem with this approach is that there are biblical passages that tell us that Christian husbands or wives must sometimes endure hardship because of the behavior of an unbelieving or professedly Christian spouse (see particularly Peter's counsel to wives in 1 Peter 3:1-6 in light of 1 Peter 2:13-25). Where situations like this exist, the general biblical counsel is to endure suffering patiently as Christ did.

These factors lead us to be very reluctant to suggest the use of temporary physical separation at all. And again, we are speaking only of a temporary removal from the physical presence of the offending spouse, not legal separation, which we believe should be avoided whenever possible. In no case, however, should separation be used as a pressure tactic.

6. Desertion by an Unbelieving Spouse

Q: My wife professed to be a Christian when we were married, but after several years she became enamored with a false religion. Despite my earnest attempts to dissuade her, she moved out last year. This past week I received divorce papers in the mail with a note demanding that I give my signed consent for the dissolution of our marriage. I do not see any hope for her return, but I also do not believe Christians may divorce their spouses. What should I do?

A: Biblically, you are permitted to sign the papers agreeing to the divorce. In fact, your wife's demanding letter would lead us to believe that your refusal to sign would only create further contention between the two of you. Paul expressly provided for this type of situation in 1 Corinthians 7:15-16. He allowed for believers to cooperate in a divorce if the unbelieving spouse insists on it. Had your wife not filed for the divorce herself, your obligation would have been to continue working toward reconciliation. But since she, being an unbeliever, is demanding a divorce despite your earnest attempts to bring about reconciliation, you should "let [her] leave" (1 Cor. 7:15).[49] The divorce will not free you to remarry, but you are "not bound" to slavishly cling to this marriage.

7. Initiating or Participating in Legal Action When Being Divorced by an Unbeliever

Q: I am being divorced by my unbelieving wife, and she is seeking full custody of our three children. I am concerned that if custody is granted to her, the children will suffer by being raised primarily in an ungodly home. Does my cooperation in this divorce on the basis of 1 Corinthians 7:15-16 leave me with no legal options? Am I required to passively comply with whatever my wife demands in terms of child-custody or financial matters?

A: In situations involving the custody of children, there is obviously the potential for disagreement and strife in the divorce process. In our view, even though the believer should maintain a cooperative

---

49 Paul makes no comment concerning which spouse (i.e., the believer or the unbeliever) must move out of the house. This determination must be made on an individual basis depending on the circumstances. When Paul speaks of the unbelieving spouse leaving, he is speaking of leaving the marriage (i.e., divorce).

demeanor, a certain degree of shrewdness and the employment of appropriate legal measures is valid in these situations and may be necessary in order to preserve the children's well-being. Even when cooperating in a divorce initiated by an unbelieving spouse, believers have a competing obligation to bring up their children "in the discipline and instruction of the Lord" (Eph. 6:4). This obviously means maintaining regular access to the children for the purpose of teaching them the gospel and taking them to the meetings of the church. It also entails keeping them out of spiritually harmful environments as much as possible.

Furthermore, a believer may contend legally (in a dignified manner, of course) for what is reasonable and right in terms of the financial dissolution of the marriage when an unbelieving spouse sues for divorce. Paul instructs Christians not to take legal action against other *Christians* (1 Cor. 6:1-8), but nothing is said that would prevent a Christian from using the legal system to settle a dispute with an unbeliever. Even Paul made use of the Roman legal system by appealing to Caesar in his dispute with unbelieving Jews (Acts 25:11).

8. Initiating or Participating in Legal Action When Being Divorced by a Believer

Q: I am a Christian, and I am certain that my husband is one too. Recently, however, due to various stresses and problems in our marriage, he informed me that he plans to file for divorce. I told him that I am against the divorce, and I encouraged him to seek counsel from our pastor, but it does not appear that he will change his mind. What are my biblical obligations and responsibilities in terms of cooperation and involvement in court proceedings? Should I cooperate for the sake of peace when being divorced by another believer? If he does go through with the divorce, am I allowed to use the court system to protect myself and pursue justice?

A: The only case in which Paul expressly permitted a Christian to cooperate in a divorce is when the divorce is initiated by an *unbelieving* spouse (1 Cor. 7:15). There is no biblical passage that would appear to provide an exception to this limitation when a divorce is sinfully initiated by another Christian. You may also be aware that the apostle Paul sharply criticized Christians who were using the public legal system to settle disputes with other Christians. Paul wrote,

> Does any one of you, when he has a case against his neighbor, dare to go to law before the unrighteous and not before the saints? Or do you not know that the saints will judge the world? If the world is judged by you, are you not competent to constitute the smallest law courts? Do you not know that we will judge angels? How much more matters of this life? So if you have law courts dealing with matters of this life, do you appoint them as judges who are of no account in the church? I say this to your shame. Is it so, that there is not among you one wise man who will be able to decide between his brethren, but brother goes to law with brother, and that before unbelievers? Actually, then, it is already a defeat for you, that you have lawsuits with one another. Why not rather be wronged? Why not rather be defrauded? On the contrary, you yourselves wrong and defraud. You do this even to your brethren. (1 Cor. 6:1-8)

This passage makes it clear that a Christian appealing to the public legal system to settle a dispute with another Christian constitutes a sinful failure, not only on the part of the Christian who initiates the legal action, but also on the part of the local church. Legal matters between Christians should be settled by appealing to wise Christian leaders. In most cases these will be the pastors/elders of a local church working with other wise men in the church who are able to hear both sides of a matter and decide on a godly resolution. In some cases, outside counsel may be sought from Christians who have expertise in particular areas, but even in these cases the local church should give the final ruling. Once a matter has been resolved in this way, it should be seen as binding, just as though it had been resolved in a court of law.

This type of "church court" is only appropriate when two *believers* have a dispute. If a believer has a legal dispute with an *unbeliever*, there is no sin in using the public legal system to settle the matter. Determining whether one is dealing with a true Christian, or with an unbeliever who has formerly maintained an outwardly Christian appearance is often difficult. In your situation, involvement on the part of the local church may help to clarify your husband's true spiritual condition.

True Christians can suffer temporary lapses in obedience to God due to neglect of prayer, absence from Christian fellowship, inconsistency in spiritual disciplines, or even physical issues like depression or mental illness. The fact that a person commits a serious sin should not automatically lead us to conclude that he or she is not a Christian, but we should also be willing to recognize that a person everyone *thought* was a believer may not actually be one.

The way a person responds to correction from other Christians often reveals his or her true spiritual condition. If the leaders of your local church were to become involved, not only by counseling, but also rebuking your husband for his intention to divorce you, he might repent. Repentance would be a blessing, and it would strengthen everyone's assurance that he is a true Christian. However, if he were confronted by you (Matt. 18:15), then by two or three others (Matt. 18:16), and then by the church as a whole (Matt. 18:17), but refused to repent of his intention to divorce you, the obligation of the church would be to consider him an unbeliever. This is not to say for sure that he *is* an unbeliever, but in obedience to Christ the church has no legitimate choice but to *consider* him an unbeliever (Matt. 18:17). If this were to happen in your case, it would be appropriate for you to respond to your husband's initiation of a divorce as one would respond to an unbeliever (1 Cor. 7:15). You would also be permitted to initiate legal action after your husband has filed for divorce in order to seek justice in terms of child custody matters or financial settlements.

In summary, once a Christian realizes that his or her Christian spouse is refusing to relent from the determination to initiate a divorce, only one course of action is immediately necessary: obedience to Christ's instructions in Matthew 18:15-17. Once the matter is given to the church, three outcomes are possible:

1. Your husband may repent when the matter is addressed by your church. In this event you should forgive him and seek

biblical counsel concerning the issues that led to the marital crisis, with the hopeful end that your marriage will be fully restored.

2. Your church may address the matter biblically by calling your husband to repentance, first privately, then publicly, but he may refuse to admit the wrong and continue moving toward divorce. In this event, the church should consider him an unbeliever (Matt. 18:17) and remove him from membership. Because the situation now involves a man everyone in the church should consider an unbeliever (despite his continuing claim to be a Christian), you are free to cooperate in the divorce and use the public legal system as needed.

3. Your church may neglect its disciplinary responsibility altogether, or may begin properly but fail to see the matter to a biblical conclusion. In this case, you would be left in an incredibly difficult situation. You should, in our opinion, seek the wisest, most biblical counsel available, even if this means going to someone other than your pastor, and come to your own private determination as to whether your husband is a believer or an unbeliever. Then, having arrived at that conclusion, you should act according to that determination.

We hope this section underscores the importance of belonging to a local church in which biblical church discipline is faithfully practiced. As you can see, where local churches fail to exercise their obligation to become directly involved in these matters, Christians are often left with no good answers and no clear course of action. Sadly, those who are left in such predicaments often feel as though they have no choice but to rely on the public legal system to settle disputes *between true Christians*, though prohibited by Paul. The church may be largely at fault in such cases, and we certainly empathize with believers who find themselves in these predicaments, but we cannot endorse any Christian's decision to go against the plain words of Scripture.

16

Questions About Remarriage After Divorce

The fact that the one-flesh union created by God in marriage remains intact even after divorce leads inevitably to difficult questions. The questions are particularly troublesome when one spouse marries someone else while the original spouse is living. One might ask, for example, "Does a second marriage bring about a second one-flesh union even though the first one-flesh union remains?" This first question naturally leads to another: "Can a person be 'one flesh' with two (or more) people at the same time?"

Part of the difficulty with these two questions is that they are never answered directly in the Bible. They can only be answered by reasoning through the related biblical commands and principles. Having carefully thought through the relevant biblical statements and principles, we believe the answer to the first question above is "Yes, *every* marriage is the joining of a man and a woman by God in a permanent one-flesh union." We base this answer primarily on the fact that no qualitative distinction is ever made in Scripture between first and second (or subsequent) marriages. The authors simply refer to marriages as "marriages," husbands as "husbands," and wives as "wives," whether concerning first marriages, second marriages, or more. This is true even in the Old Testament where polygamy was the common practice. Though Jacob married Leah first, for example, Rachel was just as much his "wife" as Leah (Gen. 29:28). Later, when Jacob intended to leave Laban's service, he said,

"Give me my *wives* and my children . . . and let me depart" (Gen. 30:26, emphasis added). It logically follows, then, to answer the second question by saying "Yes, a person *can* be 'one flesh' with two (or more) people at the same time."[50]

Another issue that presents itself to the person who thinks through the remarriage dilemma is even more difficult to address: Assuming (as we do in this book) that a second one-flesh union is established in a second marriage while the former one-flesh union remains intact, what is the nature of the continuing one-flesh union with a former spouse? What obligations (if any) remain with respect to the first union, and how should (or how can) these obligations be fulfilled? Should they be fulfilled at all in light of the new vows of exclusive devotion to the second spouse? Also, what terminology should be used to define this dual one-flesh union?

Again, the Bible contains no explicit terminology or clear precept that would give direct answers to these questions. The biblical commands and principles related to marriage, however, lead us to conclude that in terms of faithful and active devotion to a husband or wife, a second marriage after divorce should be treated as the only existing marriage. No one should forget or deny that a first marriage existed, or that the divorce of the former spouse and the marriage to the second spouse were sinful acts which may have continuing consequences, but those who have sinned in this way should not think of themselves as still married to their former spouse(s). The act of remarriage after divorce constitutes a binding commitment of complete devotion to the new spouse, as well as an irreversible decision to leave previous marital obligations forever unmet.[51] Because some scholars have described subsequent marital unions while a former spouse is still living as a form of polygamy, we have addressed the validity of this terminology in scenario 11 below.

---

50 We are not implying that the example of Jacob and his two wives serves as conclusive proof that a second marriage after a divorce forms a second intact one-flesh union. There was no divorce or remarriage in Jacob's case, so the situation was obviously different than what we are discussing in this book. We simply offer this example to demonstrate that a single person can be united in two one-flesh unions at the same time.

51 This is not to say that relationships with children from former marriages should cease once a divorced person has remarried, or that child-support and/or alimony obligations are rendered null and void by the remarriage. These relationships and responsibilities remain.

Another difficult question that arises concerns the moral status of the ongoing sexual relationship in a subsequent marriage while a former spouse is living. Are the husband and wife in a subsequent marriage following a divorce committing repeated acts of adultery, or was there only a single act of adultery when the marriage began? We have addressed this matter in scenario 10 below.

Finally, it should be noted that these difficult questions do not only plague those who hold a no remarriage position. Every Christian who believes that there are *any* biblical restrictions related to remarriage must deal with these issues when a remarriage occurs that is not permissible according to their particular view. The only people who find themselves completely unencumbered by dilemmas like these are those who believe there can be no such thing as a wrongful marriage after divorce.

9. Second Marriages While Former Spouses are Living

Q: I have already divorced and remarried but my former spouse is still alive. I now realize that I committed adultery when I remarried, but what should I do now?

A: You should view your current marriage as a merciful blessing from God and stay married. You have made vows of commitment to your second spouse, and vows should not be broken (Eccl. 5:5). Additional sins (i.e., divorcing *again*) can do nothing to make amends for former sins. God can, and often does, bless second marriages despite the fact that they were entered into sinfully (often due to ignorance of biblical teaching). Furthermore, we do not see any extreme reaction in the New Testament to situations where wrongful second marriages undoubtedly existed. For example, Jesus repeatedly stated that to marry a divorced person is adultery, but He never suggested that a second divorce should occur. When Paul wrote to the Christians in Corinth, he was certainly aware that some of them had divorced in the past and were now remarried to a different husband or wife. Divorce and remarriage were rampant in that culture. Yet even in this social context, Paul not only told the Corinthians that they should not divorce (1 Cor. 7:10-13), he also instructed them to remain sexually active with their current spouses (1 Cor. 7:1-5). Clearly Paul did not see any need to end wrongful second marriages.[52]

Christians occasionally find themselves reviewing their former activities in life and learning, with deep regret, that actions they thought legitimate at the time were, in fact, sinful. In the area of marital sin, wrongful remarriage after divorce is not the only way this could happen. It could also happen if a believer were to marry an unbeliever before discovering that such marriages are prohibited in the Bible (1 Cor. 7:39). A marriage that began with an act of adultery is nonetheless a true marriage and should be nourished and cherished as such, much the same as a child conceived as the result of an extramarital affair is a wonderful creation of God and should be accepted and cared for. In both of these situations, the sin (i.e., adultery) that brought about the result (i.e., the marriage or the child) does not affect the status or value of the result itself. The sin of adultery simply calls for repentance before God.

10. Wrongful Second Marriages and the Question of Ongoing Adultery

Q: Five years ago I selfishly divorced my wife and married another woman. I understand now that my second marriage was an act of adultery. But what is the current status of my relationship with my second wife. Am I committing repeated acts of adultery?

A: There is no doubt that your second marriage was an *act* of adultery (Matt. 5:32; 19:9; Mark 10:11-12; Rom. 7:2-3). But in our view, there is no reason to think of yourself as committing a *new* act of adultery every time you and your second wife engage in sexual relations. This distinction is based on two factors:

1. When Jesus referred to wrongful remarriage as adultery, He was speaking of the point-in-time act of entering into the second marriage. Technically, the present tense Greek verb translated "commits adultery" can be understood as depicting either present ongoing action or a single act that occurs at a point in time. The context in this case seems to

---

52 Some may question this conclusion on the basis of the divorces recorded in Ezra 9 and 10. For our discussion of this passage, see appendix 1.

demand the latter meaning.[53] Jesus said, "*Whoever marries a divorced woman* [an act which obviously occurs at a single point in time] *commits adultery* [describing the sin that occurs at the same point in time]" (Matt. 5:32, emphasis added, cf. Matt. 19:9; Mark 10:11-12; Luke 16:18).

Some may claim, on the basis of Romans 7:3, that a woman in a second marriage after divorce is "called an adulteress" because she is involved in an *ongoing* sexual relationship with her second husband. We would argue that the label "adulteress" does not necessarily lead to this conclusion. One need not be a serial killer to be called a murderer, or steal habitually to be called a thief. The commission of a single crime is sufficient to warrant the application of these labels. Likewise, the commission of a single act of adultery in consummating a wrongful second marriage is sufficient to warrant the application of the label, "adulteress." Leviticus 20:10 solidly affirms this point, saying, "If there is a man who commits adultery with another man's wife [clearly allowing for the possibility that this may be a single act of adultery] . . . the *adulterer* and the *adulteress* shall surely be put to death" (emphasis added).

2. In 1 Corinthians 7:1-5, Paul commands Christian couples, as well as Christians who are married to unbelievers, to continue (or reestablish) sexual relations with one another. Given the fact that divorce and remarriage were rampant in the culture of Corinth and other Mediterranean cities (as is commonly acknowledged by historians), Paul certainly must have realized that some of the married couples to whom he was writing (in addition to others who would read and apply his words later) were in second marriages. It would be particularly unreasonable to insist, for example, that none of the *unbelieving* spouses in Corinth had been previously married to another person who was still alive. But if repeated sexual relations in a wrongful second marriage were rightly described as an ongoing form of adultery, Paul would not have permitted them to continue.

---

53 See J. Carl Laney, *The Divorce Myth* (Minneapolis: Bethany House, 1981), 120-121.

11. The Question of Polygamy

Q: I am a divorced and remarried man. My first wife is still alive. According to your view, the one-flesh union with my first wife is still intact, *and* I have a second one-flesh union with my second wife. Do I have two wives? Am I a polygamist?

A: Some Christian teachers and authors maintain that remarriage after divorce while a former spouse is living is similar to, if not a form of, polygamy (i.e., having more than one wife at the same time) or polyandry (i.e., having more than one husband at the same time). We understand how this conclusion is reached logically. Since the *one-flesh union* exists until death, it is often argued that the *marriage* still exists. If this is indeed a correct application of marital terminology, then it would be proper to say that a man who has divorced and remarried has two wives (polygamy), and a woman who has divorced and remarried has two husbands (polyandry). As one author notes, "Since the first marriage is, according to Christ, not at an end, the analogies with polygamy are inescapable."[54]

The use of polygamy/polyandry terminology to describe second marriages after divorce initially appears to be validated by Paul's words in 1 Corinthians 7:39 and Romans 7:2. Both of these verses tell us that a woman is "bound" (referring to the marriage bond) until the death of the man called "her husband." Since the one to whom she is bound is referred to as "her husband," and since only death releases her from that bond, it is reasoned that he must still be "her husband" even after she has divorced him and married another man. Despite this apparent support for the use of polygamy/polyandry terminology, the correct way of labeling this post-divorce, second-marriage relationship is not so easily determined. In fact, we believe there are four biblical reasons why the words polygamy and polyandry should *not* be used to describe the condition of someone who has remarried wrongfully.

1. When the Samaritan woman at the well said to Jesus, "I have no husband," He replied, "You have correctly said, 'I have no husband'" (John 4:17). Though she had been married and divorced five times, Jesus affirmed her claim to be *without a husband*. He then went on to explain what He knew about

---

54 Cornes, *Divorce and Remarriage: Biblical Principles and Pastoral Practice*, 403.

her, saying, "For you have had five husbands, and the one whom you now have is not your husband; this you have said truly" (4:18). The point is, Jesus did not say, "You *have* five husbands." In other words, He did not describe her marital status in a way that would meet the definition of polyandry. Most importantly, He did not merely *refrain* from describing her in a way that would amount to polyandry while leaving that possibility open. He made a plain statement that ruled it out as a possibility (i.e., "You have correctly said, 'I have no husband.' ").

2. In 1 Corinthians 7:11, Paul describes the situation of a woman who divorces her husband as that of being "unmarried," which is the same as saying she has no husband (as Jesus said to the woman in John 4). When Paul goes on to say that if she does divorce she must remain unmarried "or else be reconciled to her husband," it is important to remember that he is not referring to a woman who has *already* divorced. He is referring to a woman who is currently married and *should not* divorce. The man Paul calls "her husband" is the man who is *currently* her husband. Paul never says, or even implies, that this man would still be called "her husband" even if she were to divorce him. This same principle should be applied to 1 Corinthians 7:39 and Romans 7:2-3.

3. In Deuteronomy 24:1-4, the woman who has been divorced and remarried is described as "another man's wife" (v. 2). Two verses later, in the event that the second marriage has ended, Moses tells the Israelites that "her *former* husband who sent her away is not allowed to take her *again to be* his wife" (v. 4, emphasis added). There would be no logic in calling this man her former husband and then prohibiting him from taking her again to be his wife if she were still his wife even though they had divorced.

4. No biblical author applies polygamy/polyandry terminology to the person who has committed the sin of adultery by remarrying after divorce.

In our view you are not a polygamist or bigamist[55] since you are not actually married to two people at the same time. When a marriage ends in divorce, the union that remains intact is no longer correctly identified as a "marriage." Former husbands and wives are no longer to be thought of (or spoken of) as "husbands" or "wives." The Bible typically uses the term "one flesh" to describe the permanent union that begins with marriage and continues even after divorce,[56] while using the terms "marriage," "husband," and "wife" to describe that which is ended by divorce.

Finally, it is important to remember that this is only a debate about terminology, not a question about whether remarriage after divorce is right or wrong. Whether or not we use the terms "polygamy" and "polyandry," Jesus told us that remarriage after divorce is "adultery."

12. Other Christians' Views of Second Marriages

Q: I now understand that my divorce and remarriage were sinful acts. But when other Christians learn that I divorced my wife and remarried wrongfully, won't they look down on me or consider my existing marriage second-rate?

A: We cannot assure you that no one will hold this attitude, but they should not. Where there has been repentance, forgiveness is the proper response to those who have divorced and/or remarried wrongfully—the same as toward any other past sin. As Jesus said in Luke 17:3, "If your brother sins, rebuke him; and if he repents, forgive him."

---

55 Polygamy and bigamy are often used as synonyms, but there is a technical difference. Polygamy would be best defined as the state of being married to more than one wife at a time, while bigamy is the civil crime of entering into a second marriage when you are already married to someone else. In other words, polygamy is having more than one wife, while bigamy is taking a second wife.

56 The only exception to the Bible's use of "one flesh" terminology to describe the permanent bond created by God in marriage is found in 1 Corinthians 6:16. There Paul uses "one flesh" terminology to describe a sexually immoral union that is not permanent or morally binding. For more on this, see scenario 19, "Marriage After Premarital Sexual Immorality," in chapter 17.

17

More Questions About
Remarriage After Divorce

13. The Remarriage of a Christian to an Unbelieving
Former Spouse

Q: I divorced my husband while we were both unbelievers, and
neither of us ever remarried. I am now a Christian, but he is still an
unbeliever. When Paul says that a Christian may marry "only in the
Lord," does that mean I may not marry my former husband unless
he becomes a Christian?

A: This is a difficult question to answer because there are biblical
factors that might seem to justify answering in both ways. First,
on the side of answering, "No," Paul did say, "only in the Lord," as
you quoted (1 Cor. 7:39). Elsewhere he commanded, "Do not be
bound together with unbelievers" (2 Cor. 6:14). Here Paul was not
speaking specifically about marriage, but the principle still seems
to apply. From these two passages the matter might seem clear-cut.
Many Bible teachers would answer, "You should hope and pray that
your unbelieving former husband becomes a Christian, but if this
never happens, you may not marry him."

On the side of answering, "Yes," we would note that even though
you divorced your husband, you are bound with him in a one-flesh
union that will remain intact until one of you dies. Remaining
unmarried actually prevents you from fulfilling the promises you
made at your wedding. Furthermore, Paul said clearly that he did
not want believers to divorce their unbelieving spouses (1 Cor.
7:12-13). From this we learn that once a person is joined to an
unbeliever in marriage, it is not sinful to *stay* joined. Paul's reason

for this was expressed in 1 Corinthians 7:14 where he says, "For the unbelieving husband is sanctified through his wife, and the unbelieving wife is sanctified through her believing husband." In other words, the unbelieving spouse benefits by living with a believing spouse. Peter speaks of the same benefit for a disobedient (i.e., unbelieving) husband when he says that such men "may be won without a word by the behavior of their wives, as they observe your chaste and respectful behavior" (1 Pet. 3:1-2). Based on these passages, it seems that remarriage would be permissible.

When all factors are weighed, it appears to us that it is not sinful for a Christian to remarry a former spouse who is still an unbeliever, as long as neither is bound to another living spouse. Paul's prohibition in 1 Corinthians 7:39 ("only in the Lord") was addressing the liberty a Christian has when a spouse has died. It was intended to prevent a believer from *becoming* bound to an unbeliever, not to prevent one from *remaining in* or *renewing* a bond that already exists. His words in 2 Corinthians 6:14 seem to carry the same intent. So we would say, cautiously, that as long as neither of you are otherwise forbidden to remarry (i.e., because of another existing one-flesh union), your remarriage to your former husband is permissible even though he is an unbeliever. Though we think we have the mind of God in giving this answer, we are unable to be absolutely sure.

14. The Remarriage of a Christian to a Believing Former Spouse

Q: My wife and I were believers when we divorced. We have both remained single, and have since come to understand that our divorce was sinful. We would like to remarry. May we do this?

A: Paul directly addresses this situation in 1 Corinthians 7:10-11: "But to the married I give instructions, not I, but the Lord, that the wife should not leave her husband (but if she does leave, she must remain unmarried, or else be reconciled to her husband), and that the husband should not divorce his wife." Based on this passage the answer to your question is clear: As believers, you may remarry. In fact, Paul's words seem to carry a tone of warning: If you do not remarry, your only other option is lifelong singleness. Additionally, given other New Testament passages about love, forgiveness, and reconciliation between Christians, the restoration of your marriage is what every Christian should hope for.

We would also note that reconciliation is not merely a formal agreement to marry, move back into the same home, and refer to each other as husband and wife. Reconciliation requires the removal of enmity and the renewal of mutual affection and trust. It includes the restoration of friendship and concern for the other person's well-being. It also involves the desire and intention to resume exclusive faithfulness in sexual relations.

Also, remember that the two of you are *not* currently married just because the one-flesh union is still intact. By divorcing, although you did not destroy the one-flesh union, you *did* end the marriage. The only way you may resume marital intimacy is through another recognized marriage according to the requirements of the society in which you live (cf. Rom. 13:1-2; 1 Pet. 2:13-15). You also may not cohabitate or behave in other ways as though you are "husband and wife" unless you marry.

15. Remarriage to a Former Spouse After a Second Divorce

Q: My first wife and I divorced hastily a number of years ago following a single instance of adultery on my part. My wife never remarried, but I did. After about five years, my second marriage ended in divorce. Recently my first wife and I have been considering the prospects of getting remarried to each other. May we do that?

A: Based on the principles of divorce and remarriage as explained by Christ and Paul, our answer to your question would be twofold:

- If the second marriage has ended in divorce and the second spouse is still living, it is *not* lawful to return to the first spouse. A second one-flesh union was created in the second marriage and remains intact despite the divorce. Therefore, to return to the first spouse would be an act of adultery against the second spouse (cf. Mark 10:11-12).

- If the second marriage ended with the death of the second spouse, or if it ended in divorce but the second spouse has since died, it *is* permissible to remarry the first spouse (provided he or she is similarly free from any existing one-flesh union to another person). Jesus' concern in the

New Testament was with adultery, and there could be no adultery in this case because the one-flesh union with the second spouse was dissolved by his or her death (Rom. 7:3; 1 Cor. 7:39).

One objection to our answer might come from the way some interpreters understand Deuteronomy 24:1-4. There we are given a hypothetical situation that is similar (though not identical) to yours: A husband has divorced his wife. The wife has then gone on to marry another man. In the event that this second marriage ends in divorce (or even if the second husband were to die), the wife was not permitted to remarry her first husband. As Moses wrote, "her former husband who sent her away is not allowed to take her again to be his wife, since she has been defiled; for that is an abomination before the Lord, and you shall not bring sin on the land which the Lord your God gives you as an inheritance" (v. 4). Nothing specific is said about *how* the woman was defiled or *why* such a remarriage would be an abomination before the Lord, but remarriage to the former spouse after the second marriage ended was forbidden.

Some say that since the prohibition of remarriage to the first husband in verse 4 is never expressly nullified or qualified in the New Testament, it is still binding. Others contend that this law was uniquely applicable to the Old Testament nation of Israel. Those who take this second stance base their opinion on the fact that the prohibited remarriage was said to "bring sin on the land which the Lord your God gives you as an inheritance." In other words, their argument is that the law in Deuteronomy 24:1-4 had a specific purpose, for a specific situation, and for a specific group of people living in a specific geographical region. Therefore (according to this argument) it is no longer applicable for Christians.

We remain uncertain as to exactly why remarriage to the first husband was prohibited in Deuteronomy 24:4, particularly in the event that the second husband had died. In this event, the former one-flesh union would have ended, and only one would remain— that with the first husband. It is this puzzling factor, among others, that leads us to agree with those who believe Deuteronomy 24:1-4 had a unique application for Old Testament Israel. Most scholars who have examined divorce and remarriage in detail tend to arrive at the same conclusion. John Murray, for example, refers to Deuteronomy 24:4 as one of "the temporary regulations of the Old Testament." We agree with Murray when he writes, "It is apparent that the permission of Deuteronomy 24:1-3 [i.e., Moses' tolerance of divorce] was abrogated by our Lord. . . . [Therefore] it would hardly be feasible to regard the prohibition of Deuteronomy 24:4 as still applicable under the New Testament."[57]

16. Remarriage After a Divorce that Occurred Prior to Conversion

Q: I was divorced and remarried prior to becoming a Christian, and I was not married when I became a Christian. I have been told that on the basis of 2 Corinthians 5:17 ("Therefore if anyone is in Christ, he is a new creature; the old things passed away; behold, new things have come"), I am now a new creature, with a "clean slate," and may marry a Christian if I desire, even though my former spouse is still alive. Is this true?

A: No, in our view it is not. The requirement of either singleness or remarriage to your former spouse (as in 1 Cor. 7:10-11) was not wiped away at your conversion. We say this for three reasons:

1. Jesus appeals to God's creative, *pre-Christian* design for marriage (Gen. 1:27; 2:24) in reaffirming the permanence of the one flesh union (Matt. 19:4-6; Mark 10:6-9). God's laws for marriage, in other words, are not uniquely for Christians, but for all people *from the beginning*. This is not unusual in Scripture. Other sins committed before a person has become a Christian, though completely forgiven in Christ, nevertheless lead to continuing requirements and consequences after conversion. For example, the converted thief is still morally obliged to pay restitution for crimes committed as an unbeliever (Luke 19:8-9).

   As another example, the person who committed first-degree murder prior to becoming a Christian is still subject to the death penalty according to Genesis 9:6—"Whoever sheds man's blood, by man his blood shall be shed, for in the image of God He made man." Nothing Paul says in

---

57 Murray, *Divorce*, 113.

2 Corinthians 5:17 would give a convicted murderer a "clean slate" in terms of practical consequences just because he became a Christian *after* committing the murder. On this same principle, remembering that the permanence of marriage also stems from God's creative design of the world, 2 Corinthians 5:17 does not permit remarriage after divorce just because the person became a Christian *after* the divorce occurred.

2. When Jesus taught about divorce and remarriage He was addressing believers and unbelievers. His disciples were present, but so were the unbelieving Pharisees. Yet Jesus gave only one set of instructions regarding divorce and remarriage, making no distinction in the application of His words to one group or the other. He also said nothing that would point to the necessity of determining *when* a divorce occurred (i.e., pre- or post-conversion) in order to know whether or not remarriage is permitted.[58]

17. Remarriage of a Divorced Person After the Former Spouse Has Died

Q: My husband divorced me several years ago but has since died. Jesus said, "whoever marries a divorced woman commits adultery." Even though my husband has died, I am still "a divorced woman." Does this mean I am not permitted to remarry?

A: Jesus did not prohibit the remarriage of a divorced woman because of what she is called, but rather because she is still joined to her husband in a one-flesh union. Where this union is still in existence, remarriage is adultery. But there can be no adultery where there is no one-flesh union, and there can be no one-flesh union where a former spouse has died (as proved by Rom. 7:3 and 1 Cor. 7:39). Being formerly divorced is no barrier to marriage now that your former husband has died.

---

58 It is possible that in 2 Corinthians 5:17 Paul was not speaking of the "newness" of the individual Christian, but rather of a redemptive-historical creation in which all things are being made new in Christ. This would bring to mind not what the individual Christian has become in Christ, but what he or she has become a part of in Christ. For a compelling explanation of this understanding of the verse, see Carl Hoch, *All Things New* (Grand Rapids: Baker Books, 1995), 155-162.

18. Remarriage for the "Guilty Party" After the Death of the Former Spouse

Q: Several years ago I divorced my husband and moved in with a man with whom I was having an affair. We never married, and my husband pleaded with me to come back, but I was too hardhearted. About a year after the divorce, he was killed in an industrial accident. Following this terrible event, I left the other man, moved in with my parents, and through their influence, became a Christian. I fully recognize the evil of my mistreatment of my former husband, but I have met a godly man whom I would like to marry. He too was previously married, but his wife died of cancer. Even though my first husband is dead, a Christian friend has told me that since I was the guilty party in the divorce, I may not remarry. What would you say?

A: Your friend's counsel reflects her natural sense of justice. She cannot imagine that it would be right for you to be happily married when you were so clearly responsible for the termination of your first marriage. We certainly see her point, but we cannot find clear scriptural justification for saying that you may not remarry.

The Bible does not prohibit remarriage for the purpose of maintaining justice or fairness. As we have said before, the reason remarriage is prohibited (in every circumstance while a former spouse is living) is that it is adultery. Adultery can only take place where there is an existing union with another person. In your situation, since God has ended your previous one-flesh union through the death of your husband, and since the man you wish to marry is also free in this way, there are no other biblical reasons to prohibit your remarriage.

However, there *are* factors that you should consider before marrying again. First of all, there were personal characteristics (selfishness, lust, etc.) which led you to abandon your husband and hardheartedly refuse his pleas for reconciliation. Have you recognized and repented of those sinful traits and actions so that they will not seriously affect your new marriage? Secondly, does the man you wish to marry know how you treated your former husband? If not, you should be open and honest with him. Third, are there children involved, either from your first marriage or the man's former marriage? If so, how will they deal with the fact that you were largely responsible for the end of your first marriage? Will they be able to show you or your new husband the proper respect and honor, or will this be a source of tension? Fourth, if there are children involved from your first marriage, there will be regular contact with members of your former husband's family. Because of the way you treated him, his relatives could become a source of tension in a new marriage. When all of these factors are considered, along with the fact that even in "ideal" circumstances second marriages fail more often than first marriages, is it likely that this marriage would prosper?

19. Marriage After Premarital Sexual Immorality

Q: Before I became a Christian, I lived with a woman for several years. We were sexually active and even had a child together. This relationship is now over, although there is still a visitation arrangement concerning our daughter. Because our relationship was like a marriage in all respects except the social recognition of marriage and the vows of commitment, I have been told that I was, and still am, permanently bound to this woman in a one-flesh union as binding as marriage. Is this true?

A: First of all, we do not wish to minimize the seriousness of your former sin. Fornication is listed along with adultery and homosexuality as sins which do not characterize people who will inherit the kingdom of heaven (1 Cor. 6:9). Having said that, however, we should not make your former situation appear different than it really was. You engaged in sexual contact on a regular basis, resulting in the birth of a child, just as happens in marriage. You shared living quarters, responsibilities, and expenses, just like in marriage. There was even a certain degree of loyalty and commitment, similar to marriage. But you were no married to this woman than two teenagers who fornicate once with no resulting pregnancy.

The biblical basis for what you have been told about sexual contact resulting in a binding one-flesh union is probably 1 Corinthians 6:15-16:

Do you not know that your bodies are members of Christ? Shall I then take away the members of Christ and make them members of a prostitute? May it never be! Or do you not know that the one who joins himself to a prostitute is one body with her? For He says, "The two shall become one flesh." [quoting from Genesis 2:24]

Because Paul quotes from Genesis 2:24, it is sometimes thought that every sexual act creates a one flesh union as permanent as marriage. If this is correct, you are indeed bound to this woman. We would not say that an act of sexual immorality outside of marriage does not cause a man and a woman to become "one flesh" in some sense. Paul clearly says in the above passage that the man who joins himself to a prostitute becomes "one body with her," and he bases this on the "one flesh" language of Genesis 2:24. But there are at least four reasons to believe that the type of one-flesh union Paul spoke of here is not the same as a man and woman being permanently united in marriage:

1. Jesus tells us that it is the person who is *divorced* who may not remarry (Matt. 5:32; 19:9; Mark 10:11-12; Luke 16:18). This prohibition is never addressed to the person who has lived a pre-Christian life of sexual promiscuity *without* being married. For the divorced person, remarriage is only unlawful because the one-flesh union created by God in marriage still exists. So where there has been no actual marriage, there can be no morally binding union.

2. Throughout the Bible there are numerous references to sexual relationships that are not marriages. For example, David committed adultery with Bathsheba resulting in the conception of a child. But it was not until later, after the death of Uriah her husband, that David took her *as his wife* (2 Sam. 11:26-27). In the New Testament, Jesus informs the woman at the well that she has had five husbands, but then He says, "and the one whom you now have [plainly indicating a sexual relationship] is not your husband" (John 4:18). Something in addition to sexual contact is necessary for there to be a marriage.

3. Throughout 1 Corinthians 6 and 7 it is made abundantly clear that the Corinthians were sexually promiscuous people living in the midst of a sexually decadent society. Many of them had formerly engaged in fornication and adultery (6:9). But throughout chapter 7, unless a person was already married or divorced, Paul placed no restriction on their right to marry. In fact, to all who are not married or divorced (remembering that these were the same people he addressed in 6:9), he gave explicit permission to marry if they so chose (7:8-9, 28, 36-38). There is no indication that Paul thought of premarital sexual immorality as presenting any moral barrier to marriage.

4. God commanded Hosea to marry "a wife of harlotry" (Hosea 1:2). The New English Translation renders the phrase, "Go marry a prostitute," and comments, "The phrase 'wife of harlotries' probably refers to a prostitute, possibly a temple prostitute serving at a Baal temple."[59] This woman was obviously guilty of multiple acts of fornication (and adultery when she sinned sexually with married men) prior to her marriage to Hosea. Unlike God's marriage to Israel, this marriage was no metaphor. Hosea and Gomer were real people who produced real children. We simply cannot concede that God would command His prophet to sin by marrying a woman who was already bound in a one-flesh union with another man (actually, multiple unions with many different men). But this would be the unavoidable conclusion if every act of sex creates a permanent one-flesh union.

These factors lead us (and most interpreters) to conclude that premarital sexual contact does not form an indissoluble moral bond that would make a subsequent marriage an act of adultery.

It is difficult to know with certainty why Paul quoted from Genesis 2:24 in 1 Corinthians 6:16. He was likely emphasizing the seriousness of sexual sin by noting that the physical act is no different than the physical consummation of marriage.

---

59 The NET Bible, New English Translation, footnote 11, p. 1557.

He was obviously concerned about the seriousness of a member of Christ's body joining himself to the body of an unbeliever in a sexual manner (v. 15). In this respect, he seemed to be saying that sexual immorality committed by a Christian is a sort of adultery against Christ Himself.[60]

---

60 For a helpful examination of this text, see Fee, *The First Epistle to the Corinthians*, 257-260.

18

Questions About Divorce, Remarriage, and Church Polity

Doctrinal conclusions related to divorce and remarriage affect not only the way individual Christians conduct themselves, but also the corporate activities of the local church. Christians who are joined together in the fellowship of a local church, and who seek to obey Christ in harmony with each other, must make every effort to agree about important matters of conviction. Having agreed (or at least having arrived at a general consensus) as to what doctrinal position is correct, they must establish a church practice that is consistent with their convictions.

The authors of this book are all pastors of the same local church. Almost all of the members of our church agree that the permanence view is the biblical position. Even those who do not yet fully understand or agree with this view have stated their willingness to cooperate in church life according to these convictions. The answers to the following questions are based on our convictions and the way they are lived out in actual practice in our church.

20. Church Membership and the Permanence View

Q: Can a person be a member of your church if he or she disagrees with the permanence view?

A: Yes, in most cases. Not every member of our church will immediately or easily embrace the permanence view, and some may never come to full agreement. This difference of opinion does not, in itself, prevent anyone from becoming or remaining a member of our church. Regardless of personal convictions about divorce and remarriage, however, all members and prospective members need to be aware of the following expectations associated with membership:

- Members are encouraged to study matters related to divorce and remarriage and discuss their personal views with other members, even if they disagree with the permanence view. There are limitations to this freedom, however. No member may encourage another member to act contrary to the church's position, speak disparagingly of those who hold this view, or behave divisively in other ways.

- All members must acknowledge that the permanence view will be the guiding conviction in disciplinary matters related to divorce and remarriage.

- Members who have not embraced the permanence view must agree not to complicate and/or delay disciplinary actions related to divorce and/or wrongful remarriage by seeking to debate the permanence view during a disciplinary process.

- Any member may abstain from affirming a disciplinary action related to divorce and/or remarriage on the basis of his or her personal convictions, but all members must respect and abide by disciplinary decisions and actions deemed appropriate and necessary by the majority.

Q: You said a person who disagrees can be a member "in most cases." What is the exception to this general rule?

A: The exception concerns those who disagree with the permanence view and have divorced a spouse and/or remarried after divorce while a former spouse was still living. Divorce and wrongful remarriage are serious sins. To divorce a spouse is to disobey Christ's command not to separate what God has joined together (Matt. 19:6; Mark 10:9). To remarry after divorce while the former spouse is living is to commit an act of adultery (Matt. 5:32; 19:9; Mark 10:11-12; Luke 16:18; Rom. 7:3). As with any other significant act or pattern of sin formerly committed by a person who seeks membership with our church, sins related to divorce and remarriage must be repented of before church membership can be granted. The person needs to sincerely acknowledge that his or her former actions were sinful. Until such an acknowledgement is expressed, our church has no option but to view the person as unrepentant with respect to the sin(s) committed. It cannot be right to overlook in an unrepentant *prospective* member what would cause the disciplinary removal of an unrepentant *member*.

Q: Are you saying that you cannot receive these people because they are not Christians?

A: No, that is not what we are saying. We are sensitive to the widespread influence of conservative, Bible-believing Christians who, for centuries, have taught that divorce and remarriage are permitted in cases of adultery or desertion by a disobedient spouse. Some who seek membership with our church, and who have divorced a spouse and/or remarried after divorce, may have been fully convinced that their actions were permissible on the basis of this prevailing view. Even a sincere believer could misconstrue a few Bible verses as permitting divorce and/or remarriage in cases of adultery or desertion (specifically Matt. 5:32; 19:9; 1 Cor. 7:15, 27-28). While we are firmly convinced of the view we now hold, the confusion among well-meaning, Bible-believing Christians is understandable.

Q: Are you adding to the basic requirements for church membership (i.e., conversion and baptism) by insisting upon repentance in this specific area?

A: No, we do not believe we are. The practice of dealing with former sinful actions in the membership process is common to churches who work hard to maintain a regenerate membership. Discussions about former sins are not focused only on the issue of divorce and remarriage. *Any* notable sins for which a church would enact discipline are part of the intimate discussions with prospective members. We welcome all who are repentant of known sins, because repentance is one necessary mark of a true Christian.

In the end, we are asking people in this category to enter into membership with the same attitude toward their former divorce(s) and/or remarriage(s) as toward any other former sins—that is, with a heartfelt acknowledgment of *whatever* sin was involved. Depending on the circumstances of the individual divorce and/or remarriage, this acknowledgment of past sin may focus more on the act(s) of disobedience than on an attitude of rebellion, because the sin may have been committed without knowledge of error or premeditation.

Q: Why would you require repentance prior to membership in the case of a person who did not know or understand biblical instructions regarding divorce and remarriage, or one who knows the Bible and is fully convinced that he or she did what God permits?

A: In the civil realm, ignorance of the law does not exempt a person from facing the consequences of the law. The same is true when a person misinterprets the law and, as a result, does what is unlawful. Such a person may be less culpable because his crime was not committed intentionally, but he or she was nonetheless disobedient to his government. We believe this is a biblical pattern as well. For Old Testament Jews there was a category of sin called "unintentional." There was even a special sacrifice prescribed for such sins. Before the sacrifice was offered, however, the sin(s) committed in ignorance had to be brought to the guilty person's attention by others. Then, by offering a sacrifice, the guilty person acknowledged his or her actions as sinful. This acknowledgement through sacrifice for unintentional sin was required for leaders as well as common people (Lev. 4:22-31).

This old covenant law is instructive in principle for us as new covenant believers. We too may be guilty before we realize we have sinned, but when our sin is made known to us, repentance is required. This principle is evident in Jesus' instructions in Matthew 18:15-17, in that additional witnesses, sometimes even the whole church, must seek to convince the offending person that he or she has sinned.

We want to deal with each prospective member lovingly on this issue, and with grace. We realize that a new understanding of the sinfulness of past actions may be hard to receive and almost startling, especially if sincere efforts were made to obey God. We have struggled with a proper response to this dilemma, discussing various approaches of accommodation. We trust that all incoming members will realize that though we are conscience-bound, we will also empathize when discussing these matters. We will carefully work through the circumstances of the former divorce and/or remarriage in order to help the prospective member understand what the proper response(s) would be.

We want you to know that we have also repented of our former views on divorce and remarriage, though, similarly, we did not believe we were acting outside of God's will at the time. Our wrong views resulted in errant counsel and likely convinced some people to disobey God—a serious and dangerous sin for those who teach the Bible and pastor churches (James 3:1). Part of our sin was in the failure to go deep enough into the divorce/remarriage issue to find out the truth. It was not easy to come to this conclusion about our own culpability, but having been convinced by Scripture, we have willingly repented. Now we are asking prospective members who have acted sinfully with respect to divorce and/or remarriage to do the same. Fundamentally, we believe that taking actions that are consistent with our convictions will be more helpful for the church, the kingdom of God as a whole, the culture around us, and even the individual seeking membership. We also fully believe that these measures will prevent divorces. Most importantly, by promoting marriage permanence in this way we will be valuing and honoring marriage the way Paul did in Ephesians 5:22-33 when he likened the relationship of a husband and wife to the relationship of Christ and His church.

Q: What about already-existing members who divorced and/or remarried wrongfully according to the permanence view, were received into membership before you arrived at your new position, yet still disagree with your view? Would you enact church discipline in these cases on the basis of your new position?

A: Along with the obligation to welcome new members in a manner that is consistent with our convictions, we have the competing obligation to honor the covenant into which we entered when a person became a member. In this case, the person has done nothing since becoming a member to break the membership covenant, and the bonds of love with the church have grown strong. Breaking such a bond at this point, when no additional sins have been committed, would undoubtedly do more harm than good. Because of these factors, we intend to maintain unbroken fellowship with members who are in this category even if they are never convinced of the permanence view.

We hope that members in the above category will study the permanence position carefully and prayerfully, maintain a teachable spirit, and pursue doctrinal unity (as all members agree to do in submitting to our membership agreement[61]). Only if an already-existing member were to commit additional sin(s) related to divorce and/or remarriage, or become divisive about doctrinal differences, would church discipline be considered.

21. The Necessity of Church Discipline for Divorce and/or Remarriage

Q: Would church discipline be necessary in every instance of divorce and/or wrongful remarriage? Might there not be circumstances that are so difficult and which so powerfully compel a Christian to divorce and/or remarry that you would permit an exception in practice, even though not from a doctrinal standpoint?

A: An offending spouse's sin may cause incredibly difficult marital circumstances. These might drive even a mature Christian to believe that initiating a divorce is permitted, or that there is no other way to escape the situation. We also realize that a person who wishes to divorce can easily find a noted Christian leader and any number of popular books to affirm his or her claim that the Bible justifies divorce in his or her particular situation. But we believe it is plain in the Scriptures that Jesus prohibited divorce categorically. He said, "What therefore God has joined together, let no man

---

61 Our membership agreement may be viewed on our church's website, www.ChristFellowshipKC.org.

separate" (Matt. 19:6, Mark 10:9). Furthermore, God promises in His Word that He "will not allow [us] to be tempted beyond what [we] are able, but with the temptation will provide the way of escape also, so that [we] will be able to endure it" (1 Cor. 10:13). No matter how severe the temptation, sinful acts like divorce, or remarriage while a former spouse is living, are never the means of escape provided by God.

Our general answer with respect to the sin of divorce is that every divorce initiated by a Christian, no matter how seemingly unavoidable or justifiable, must be dealt with correctively by the local church where that Christian is a member. We would also note, however, that only the person who remains persistently unrepentant in his or her sin would be removed from membership. Up to the point where this action becomes necessary, there is freedom to apply less severe corrective measures as we seek the person's repentance.

As with the sin of divorce, the sin of wrongful remarriage must also be addressed firmly by the local church. We would not say that difficult circumstances could *never* compel a person to remarry, particularly in poorer countries where poverty might drive a divorced woman to seek a new husband for financial reasons. Something like this seemed to be the case in Matthew 5:32 where Jesus said that the man who divorces his blameless wife "makes her commit adultery." Presumably, social and cultural factors made remarriage after divorce a near necessity in first century Israel. But even in this situation, where the husband who divorced his wife bore much of the blame, Jesus also spoke of *the woman's* act of adultery in remarrying. Furthermore, desperate situations like this are not the norm. Most who remarry after divorce in our culture do so simply because they prefer marriage over singleness. Whatever the perceived need, remarriage after divorce while a former spouse is living is an act of adultery, so the local church has no right to treat this sin lightly.

Finally, note that the matter of church discipline for divorce and/ or remarriage is not only faced by churches that hold a permanence view. This issue must be faced by every church that sees *any* biblical restrictions of divorce and remarriage. For example, if a church permits its members to divorce for adultery *only*, what should happen when a member divorces for some other reason (as is all-too-common in evangelical churches today)? If a church believes remarriage is permitted only following divorce for adultery, or after desertion by an unbelieving spouse, what should happen when someone who was divorced for other reasons remarries? Every church must be prepared to enact discipline with respect to sins related to divorce and remarriage according to their own understanding of the biblical texts. Failure to enact discipline in these instances is disobedience to Christ.

22. Divorce, Remarriage, and Pastoral Qualification

Q: Is a divorced and/or remarried man automatically disqualified from holding the office of elder or deacon? Can he no longer be thought of as "the husband of one wife"?

A: We believe the term "husband of one wife" (1 Tim. 3:2, 12; Titus 1:6) is qualitative, not quantitative. The most literal way of translating the phrase is "one-woman man." It describes a man who is singularly devoted to his wife—in other words, a faithful husband. The term itself does not describe a man's present or past marital status, but rather, his reputation and currently observable qualities as a husband. Three factors led us to this conclusion:

1. The phrase, "husband of one wife" is found in a list of necessary character qualities. Paul certainly knew that the men who would be considered for eldership might have great sins in their past with respect to marriage and other issues (e.g., fornication, drunkenness, and even murder). His purpose in listing the character qualities of an elder was to limit the office to men who are *currently* known as being above reproach.

   When Paul listed "the husband of one wife" as a requirement for eldership, he was indeed ruling out those who were currently married to more than one woman (i.e., polygamists), even though this does not seem to have been an issue for early Christians. He was also excluding married men who were flirtatious or involved in adultery. There is no way such a man could be described qualitatively as "a one-woman man" because more than one woman is *currently* the object of his affections. But a man who has been divorced and remarried certainly can be a "one-woman man" in character and reputation, despite his past sins, if he has faithfully demonstrated his singular, devoted affection toward his current wife.

2. In 1 Timothy 5:9, Paul uses the same type of phrase to describe the qualities of the widows who were to be supported by the local church. He says, "A widow is to be put on the list only if she is not less than sixty years old, having been the wife of one man." As in 1 Timothy 3:2, this phrase is most literally translated, "one-man woman." The article "the" as well as the words "having been" were added for clarity.

   The phrase "one-man woman" obviously cannot refer to a widow's current marital situation. She is a widow by virtue of the fact that her husband has died. Therefore, "having been the wife of one man" clarifies that Paul was making reference to her past. But was Paul ruling out the widow who had been married twice in her life on that basis alone? What if her first husband was killed in battle at a young age and she married again, only to lose her second husband to ill health? What if she were a devoted and faithful wife to both men? Is she excluded on the basis of circumstances in which she was blameless? We think this cannot be the case. Paul was once again asking the church to examine this woman's reputation and character qualities before including her in the list of those who receive financial support. This is confirmed in 1 Timothy 5:14 where Paul instructs the younger widows to "get married." If "one-man woman" in verse 9 is quantitative and not qualitative, Paul would have been instructing these young widows to do something that would later result in their being refused church support in the event that their second husband were to die.

3. If "the husband of one wife" in 1 Timothy 3:2 and Titus 1:6 refers to a man's marital status (as opposed to the character quality of marital faithfulness), then *no* unmarried man

may be an elder. Remember that Paul said, "An overseer, then, *must be* . . . the husband of one wife" (emphasis added). If this is an absolute quantitative requirement, then the requirement works both ways. An elder must not only be the husband of *one* wife, he must *have* a wife. If the requirement were quantitative, in other words, it would disqualify the man who has never been married, as well as the existing elder whose wife dies.

Based on these three factors, we are convinced that the phrase "husband of one wife" is qualitative, not quantitative. An elder must be faithfully devoted to his current wife. Divorce, or even a wrongful remarriage somewhere in a man's past, does not automatically disqualify him from holding pastoral office.[62] Even a repentant former murderer like Paul was entrusted with a position of leadership in Christ's church, so we see no reason not to view a repentant divorcer and/or adulterer in the same way.

There are other factors related to divorce and remarriage, however, that may disqualify a divorced and/or remarried man. For example:

- Being "above reproach" (1 Tim. 3:2; Titus 1:6-7) is the overarching qualification for eldership. A man must not be subject to legitimate accusations of misconduct or questionable character. Before allowing a divorced and/ or remarried man to become an elder, a local church must carefully discern whether or not he is justifiably perceived in this way by his own children, by former churches, by co-workers, and even by the unbelieving members of the community in which he lives (1 Tim. 3:7). If past marital sins have negatively affected his personal reputation in this respect, he cannot be an elder.

- An elder must have proven himself to be a good manager of his home (1 Tim. 3:4-5). Divorce itself sometimes serves as a demonstration that this quality is lacking. A marriage might fail because of a husband's neglect of his wife and/or family responsibilities. Even when a divorce was not due

---

62 These concerns apply to deacons as well as elders.

to such neglect, other factors might demonstrate a lack in management ability. For instance, if dependent children from either his first or second marriage have become rebellious (as sometimes happens in broken marriages and second marriages), he cannot be an elder (1 Tim. 3:4-5; Titus 1:6). If his personal finances are in disarray (as often happens following a divorce) and if he has been lax in restoring order in this respect, he cannot be entrusted to manage a local church.

- Pastoral ministry is demanding. Even men who have never divorced or remarried may have difficulty managing the demands of ministry along with the needs of their wives and children. Divorce and remarriage, especially where children are involved, complicates the situation by leading to a stressful life filled with visitation arrangements, court battles, and other matters that might draw a man away from other responsibilities. Before a divorced and/or remarried man can become an elder, it must be consistently demonstrated that these effects of his divorce and/or remarriage will not unreasonably hinder his ministry.

- An elder must be held in high regard by those whom he shepherds. The members of his church must believe he is qualified to be an elder. There are many Christians who do not believe a divorced and/or remarried man may serve as an elder, based on their quantitative understanding of 1 Timothy 3:2 and Titus 1:6. Even if a divorced and/or remarried man is "above reproach" and fully qualified in every other way, if a significant number of people in his local church believe his divorce and/or remarriage automatically disqualifies him from serving as an elder, he should not seek the position of elder in that particular church.

19

A Warning About Presumptuous Sin

Presumptuous sin is sin committed *on purpose*—knowingly doing what God forbids while presuming that you will be covered by His mercy. It is an attempt to force God to apply mercy instead of justice. Sin has been called "the dare of God's justice, the rape of His mercy, the jeer of His patience, the slight of His power, and the contempt of His love."[63] All sin has these characteristics, but presumptuous sin magnifies them.

People in immensely difficult marriages may be tempted to think that getting out of the marriage would be worthwhile, even though they know that initiating a divorce is sinful. The prospect of happiness might overwhelm their commitment to obeying God. Also, because wrongful remarriage is a single act of adultery (as opposed to repeated acts of adultery through sexual intercourse with the new spouse), some may be tempted to sin presumptuously "just this once" so that they can experience the lasting joy of a second marriage. "After all," someone might think, "The Lord is gracious and forgiving. He will forgive me if I remarry wrongfully just as He forgives all my other sins. Then I will be at peace with God *and* happy in my new marriage."

Before acting out this type of reasoning, please consider four sobering truths about presumptuous sin and presumptuous sinners:

1. God hates presumptuous sin.

A purposeful, planned approach to sin reveals one of the things God hates the most. In Proverbs 6:16 we read, "There are six things

---

63 Quote attributed to John Bunyan. Original source not found.

which the Lord hates, yes, seven which are an abomination to Him." The list that follows includes pride, lying, and murder. Among these we find that God hates "a heart that devises wicked plans" (v. 18). God hates all sin, to be sure, but when you sin on purpose, your premeditated act is particularly abhorrent to Him.

2. Presumptuous sin is feared and hated by godly persons.

David pleaded with the Lord to keep him back from presumptuous sins (Ps. 19:13). He concluded his thought by saying, "Then I will be blameless, and I shall be acquitted of great transgression." People who sin presumptuously should have no confident expectation that they will be considered "blameless," or even that they will be acquitted by God.

3. True Christians are repentant sinners, not presumptuous sinners.

Regardless of the type of sin involved, those who are repentant sinners are said to be "washed," "sanctified," and "justified," while those who carelessly or intentionally continue in sin are warned not to be deceived. People of that sort, Paul tells us, "will not inherit the kingdom of God" (1 Cor. 6:9-11). Presumptuous sinners are acting like they are on their way to hell, not heaven. *They may be.*

4. Presumptuous sin often leads to disastrous consequences.

King David knew that what he was tempted to do with Bathsheba was a sin against God, but he did it anyway. In this case, his presumptuous sin brought a series of painful and tragic consequences:

- It led David into further sin—the murder of Bathsheba's husband (2 Sam. 11:14-15).

- It brought on a lengthy period of painful conviction (Ps. 32:3-4; 38:1-22; 51:3, 8, 12).

- It brought a stinging rebuke from the prophet Nathan (2 Sam. 12:1-14).

- It led to the death of the child of that union (2 Sam. 12:14-20).

- It gave occasion for the enemies of the Lord to blaspheme God (2 Sam. 12:14).

- It moved the Lord to plague David's posterity with violence, and even to raise evil against him from within his own family (2 Sam. 12:9-12).

People who presume upon God's mercy should not be surprised when they experience similar consequences. In fact, they should expect them. Perhaps it was this very experience that led David to pray this prayer:

> Also keep back your servant from presumptuous sins;
> Let them not rule over me;
> Then I will be blameless,
> And I shall be acquitted of great transgression. (Ps. 19:13)

When the sins of divorce and/or wrongful remarriage are committed presumptuously (as opposed to unintentionally or in ignorance), they are usually motivated by the notion that the sin will bring greater happiness than submission to Christ, but the anticipated happiness does not follow. Even when things *seem* to turn out as expected, the true Christian who sins presumptuously will be plagued by a guilty conscience and the chastening hand of God, both of which are far more unpleasant than the unhappiness formerly experienced in a difficult marriage or post-divorce singleness. In the end, the one who sins presumptuously is trading peace with God, fellowship with other Christians (i.e., due to church discipline), and a peaceful conscience, for a "happiness" that is not only uncertain, but also stained by sin.

Despite the gravity of presumptuous sin and the often unpleasant results of this sort of rebellion, God's forgiving mercy is great and complete. Even the person who has sinned in this way may be fully forgiven and reconciled to Him through repentance and faith in Christ.

A Final Thought

If the permanence view is God's view, it is best for Christians and unbelievers alike. More couples staying together, despite the most serious kinds of marital difficulties, will have a leavening effect on all of society. Imagine, for instance, what it would mean for a struggling couple in your extended family to remain together rather than to divorce. Though future generations may not know the difficulties they faced, they will know that they remained committed. A commitment to permanence in those preceding cannot help but promote generational stability—a momentum of faithfulness for those who follow. Our sin makes the way easier for others to sin; our obedience makes the way easier for others to obey.

We are optimistic that the permanence view will continue to find increasing acceptance among evangelicals, but we are under no illusion that everyone who reads this book will agree with us. Pain often comes with progress of this sort, but we hope the pain that results from disagreement will not be caused by harshness or bitterness on either side of this discussion. When agreement cannot be reached, godly people should always be careful to disagree in a manner characteristic of their profession.

If you do agree with us, and if you put your convictions into practice, we believe you will make an immense contribution to your extended family, your church, and your world.

Appendix 1
Comments on Secondary Old Testament Texts

Genesis 2:24 and Deuteronomy 24:1-4 are two of the Old Testament texts that address divorce and remarriage. We considered these two passages to be of primary importance because they are used by Jesus in the context of His teaching on divorce and remarriage. Aside from these two, six other Old Testament passages were considered, but not included in our main discussion: Exodus 21:7-11, Leviticus 21:7, 13-14, Deuteronomy 21:10-14, Deuteronomy 22:28-29, Ezra 9-10, and Malachi 2:16. Some of these are prescriptive texts (meaning they convey commands, permission, and/or prohibition). For the most part, however, the instructions uniquely apply to Jews under the old covenant, and/or they serve to regulate ancient Near Eastern cultural practices that were perversions of marriage (i.e., owning slave-wives and polygamy). Furthermore, none of these texts are mentioned in the New Testament. Please consider our evaluations of these passages, along with our reason(s) for not including them in Part 1 of this book.

Exodus 21:7-11

In this passage, instructions are given for a man who sells his daughter as a slave, and for the man who buys her. We did not consider this passage relevant to our discussion for three reasons:

First, the instructions were given to regulate the practice of owning and marrying slave-wives and the practice of polygamy, not marriage as it was originally designed by God. Verses 10-11, where the primary instructions are given, only apply if a second slave-wife is taken, but have no relevance where polygamy is not an accepted practice.

Second, the law spoken of in this passage was designed to protect the woman's rights, not to grant the right of divorce to her owner/ husband. The command to let a slave-wife "go out for nothing, without payment of money" (v. 11) was for the woman's benefit. It prohibited the owner/husband from retaining possession of her, or profiting financially by selling her, if he was unwilling to continue providing her with food, clothing, and conjugal rights after taking a second slave-wife. It was not intended to give him permission to divorce her.

Third, there is no mention of a divorce certificate in this text, as there is in Deuteronomy 24:1. This implies that the termination of this union was not considered the same as the termination of an ordinary marriage.

Leviticus 21:7, 13-14

In Leviticus 21:7, Jewish priests were forbidden to marry women profaned by harlotry (i.e., sexual immorality) or divorced women. The fact that priests were not allowed to marry divorced women leads many interpreters to conclude that marrying divorced women was lawful for others. Jay Adams, for example, concludes on the basis of this text that "priests are in a special class *and may not do what it is perfectly right for others to do* [emphasis original]."[64] This conclusion, however, is based on an assumption that is neither supported by the text nor necessitated by deductive reasoning. It is an unreliable interpretive practice to assume that the *presence* of a requirement for one person (or group) implies the *absence* of that requirement for everyone else. In other words, a law that says to one particular man, "You *may not* marry a divorced woman," does not necessarily imply that another man *may* marry a divorced woman.

This principle is plainly illustrated in Leviticus 21:10-15, where the Lord addresses the marital requirements of the high priest specifically. In verses 13-14 we learn that the high priest was required to marry a virgin "of his own people." If this requirement for the high priest were subjected to the above reasoning, it would seem to prove that other Jewish priests were permitted to marry women from other nations as long as they were not divorced or

---

64 Jay Adams, *Marriage, Divorce, and Remarriage in the Bible*, 85.

"profaned by harlotry" (v. 7). No reputable interpreter makes this claim, of course, because elsewhere in the Old Testament marrying foreign women was explicitly prohibited for all Jews (Deut. 7:3). This shows clearly that a requirement addressed to a specific group, or even to a single person, does not necessarily imply the absence of that requirement for everyone else. Everyone should agree that God *tolerated* the general Jewish practices of divorce and remarriage after divorce (Deut. 24:1-4; Matt. 19:8), but toleration is not the same as permission.

Leviticus 21:7, when understood in light of the rest of the Old Testament, proves nothing more than it was intended to prove: Jewish priests were required to marry either Jewish virgins or a Jewish widow (cf. Ezekiel 44:22 where the priests described in Ezekiel's vision are required to marry virgins or the widow of another priest). Leviticus 21:13-14 contains one further restriction for the high priest, prohibiting him from marrying even a widow. Because these verses specify nothing concerning non-priests, and because they contain no legislation designed to regulate divorce or remarriage, they had no significant bearing on our study.

Deuteronomy 21:10-14

This passage describes another type of slave-wife situation: A man takes a woman who was captured in battle as his slave-wife. Instructions are given to regulate her treatment if the man later becomes displeased with her. Again, we had three reasons for not including this passage in our discussion:

First, every indication is that this "marital" union was not entered into voluntarily on the woman's part, but rather was forced upon her due to her captive status. Therefore it is difficult to consider this a true marriage, since marriage involves a *covenant* commitment, which implies a *voluntary* commitment, of a man and woman to each other.

Second, similar to the instructions in Exodus 21:11, the command to "let her go" (Deut. 10:14) neither commands nor condones divorce. The purpose of the command is not to give the man *permission* to let her go, but rather to state his *obligation* to let her go instead of selling her or mistreating her.

Third, as in Exodus 21:7-11, no mention is made of a divorce certificate, even though when Moses speaks of divorce in the context of a true marriage later in this same discourse (Deut. 24:1-4), he does mention the certificate.

Deuteronomy 22:28-29

This passage anticipates the situation of a man who sexually violates a non-betrothed virgin. When such an act has been committed and is discovered, the man must pay the girl's father fifty shekels of silver and marry her. He is also prohibited from ever divorcing her. The strict prohibition of divorce in this unique situation is often thought to imply that divorce was lawful for everyone else, but this is not a necessary conclusion.

According to the same principle mentioned in our discussion of Leviticus 21:7, a law that says to a man in one particular situation, "You *may not* divorce your wife," does not necessarily imply that God's will for everyone else is, "You *may* divorce your wives." It is more biblically consistent and more logical in our view to conclude that while divorce has *never* been lawful in God's sight, He passively tolerated it due to the hardness of heart that characterized the Jews (Deut. 24:1-4; Matt. 19:8). When we read about a particular man who committed a shameful deed and was prohibited from ever divorcing his wife, the only *necessary* conclusion is that in this man's case, God's passive tolerance of divorce was withdrawn. As with Leviticus 21:7, the absence of any clear directive for men who are not in this unique situation renders it inapplicable to our study.

Ezra 9-10

In Ezra 9 and 10, a situation is recorded in which many Israelite men had disobeyed the Law of Moses by marrying foreign women (Deut. 7:3). Ezra instructed them to divorce their foreign wives in order to turn away God's anger. Some say that this passage proves that all wrongful second marriages should be terminated, but there are at least four reasons why this Old Testament text should not lead to that conclusion:

First, this was not the first time the Israelites had sinned by marrying foreign women (Judges 3:5-6, 1 Kings 11), but it is the only biblical example of correcting the problem by means of divorce. If divorcing foreign wives were God's chosen way of dealing with the persistent Jewish problem of intermarriage, we believe the practice would have been mentioned before Ezra's time.

Second, the passage describes what the Jews did in this instance, but it contains no moral commentary concerning whether or not what they did was pleasing to God. Marriages to foreign women were forbidden in the Law of Moses (Deut. 7:3), and Shecaniah's counsel to Ezra in advocating these divorces was, "let it be done according to the law" (Ezra 10:3), but nothing in the Law prescribed divorce as a corrective measure once the sin of intermarriage had been committed. Furthermore, there is no record of God instructing anyone to order these divorces, and no indication in the book of Ezra (or anywhere else in Scripture) that He approved of them.

Third, just as Old Testament Jews were not permitted to marry those outside of the old covenant (i.e., non-Jews), Christians are not permitted to marry those outside of the new covenant (i.e., non-Christians). Yet when Paul learned that Christians in Corinth were married to non-Christians, he commanded them *not* to divorce their unbelieving spouses (1 Cor. 7:12-13; cf. 1 Pet. 3:1-2). In other words, when the New Testament addresses a similar (though admittedly not identical) situation, the counsel given to Christians is directly contrary to the decision made by the Jews of Ezra's time.

Fourth, Ezra 9-10 tells the story of how the Old Testament sin of racial *inter*marriage was dealt with on one occasion, but says nothing about *re*marriage after divorce.

Based on these four factors, we did not consider Ezra 9-10 to be a prescriptive text concerning the proper response to wrongful second marriages, and therefore did not find it applicable to our study.

Malachi 2:16

This passage includes strong words about divorce and might appear to be a critical passage to address in any book on the subject. The prophet writes, "'For I hate divorce,' says the Lord, the God of Israel." Though there is some disagreement among scholars concerning the proper translation of the phrase, "For I hate divorce,"[65] Bible-believing Christians on both sides of the divorce debate agree that God hates divorce. Our purpose in writing this book was not to demonstrate from Scripture that God *hates* divorce. We sought to show that He *prohibits* it. It is theoretically possible for God to hate divorce, yet reluctantly permit it. It is also theoretically possible for Him to hate it so intensely that He prohibits it altogether. Therefore, we did not consider Malachi 2:16 to be critical for our study.

---

65 Some scholars think the phrase in Malachi 2:16 may be a reference to the man who divorces his wife, rather than to God hating divorce. In this case, it would be translated, "He hates and divorces."

Appendix 2
Bringing the Permanence View into an Established Church

Perhaps you are a pastor who has embraced the permanence view, yet you are in a church that has historically taken another position on the Bible's teaching about divorce and/or remarriage. You desire to put the permanence view into practice, but you know that immediate implementation could cause significant misunderstanding and maybe even a divided church. What can you do? Is it even possible to lead a church to affirm this position? Though your church (or even fellow elders) may never embrace the permanence view, here are some actions you can take in order to lead them in that direction:[66]

1. *Model "permanence."* In other words, if you are married, remain committed to your wife and demonstrate before the church a sacrificial love for her. If you stay at a church long enough, people will realize that your marriage is far from perfect. Yet consistent kindness toward your wife will demonstrate a Christ-like unselfishness and humility. Your spiritually healthy marriage might be a tool the Lord uses to fix broken marriages. With strong marriages multiplying, a church will accept the permanence view in practice before they are ever willing to accept it doctrinally.

2. *Preach about marriage, divorce, and remarriage, but in moderation.* With subjects like divorce and remarriage, you can say too much. There is a proper time and place

---

66 These are not necessarily in chronological order, though the reader will observe a progression.

to preach about these topics, but do not let them become the theme of your ministry. At the end of your ministry to a particular church, you should be able to say with Paul, "Therefore, I testify to you this day that I am innocent of the blood of all men. For I did not shrink from declaring to you the *whole* purpose of God" (Acts 20:26-27, emphasis added).

3. *Preach the cross and forgiveness.* In Colossians 3:13, Paul tells the church in Colossae that its relationships must be marked by a spirit of forgiveness, declaring, "Just as the Lord forgave you, so also should you." In other words, since those who are in Christ have been forgiven so much by God through the redeeming work of Christ on the cross, we likewise should be abundantly forgiving toward one another. Consider, then, how the preaching of the cross might encourage forgiveness among husbands and wives, and ultimately save marriages.

4. *Preach expositionally.* Before solid conclusions can be reached concerning what the Bible teaches about divorce and remarriage (or any subject), one must know how to study the Bible. Therefore, if we want people to understand and embrace the permanence view, they first must know how to comprehend the passages in the Bible that should lead them to such a position.

What does "expositional preaching" contribute? It will be helpful to define this type of preaching: Expositional preaching (also known as "expository preaching") happens when a preacher teaches and applies the truths of a particular passage of the Bible.[67] Therefore, expositional preaching models for people how to observe, interpret, and apply Scripture carefully.

Proper skills of interpretation are *vital* to correct conclusions. Unfortunately, good men and women sometimes come to different interpretations of Scripture, but expositional preaching can minimize these differences and help them draw conclusions based upon sound interpretive principles.

---

67 Bryan Chapell, *Christ-centered Preaching: Redeeming the Expository Sermon* (Grand Rapids: Baker, 1994), 22.

Additionally, those who preach this way typically teach consecutively through sections or entire books of the Bible. Preaching like this exposes listeners to difficult verses and even controversial subjects. For example, if a pastor decided to preach through the entire book of 1 Corinthians, he would have to deal at some point with the frequently debated issues in chapter 7.

5. **Study the relevant Scripture with the elders (or, if you do not have elders, a select group of church leaders), and put your tentative conclusions on paper.** Elders (overseers, pastors) have the primary responsibility to teach the Bible in the local church. Titus 1:9 states that a pastor should hold fast to "the faithful word which is in accordance with the teaching, so that he will be able both to exhort in sound doctrine and to refute those who contradict."

Every pastor has known the frustration of sitting through lengthy meetings where all that is discussed is the budget or dates on a calendar. Yet in order to proclaim "sound doctrine" and protect the church against harmful teaching (on a variety of subjects, including divorce and remarriage), the elders should also spend significant time together studying Scripture.

What might these study sessions look like? Initially you should seek to identify the relevant passages of Scripture for the subject at hand, and discuss these passages thoroughly in context. Between meetings, each elder should personally meditate on these Bible passages. Early in a study like this, there is a significant temptation to simply agree with what some of our favorite pastors or theologians have concluded without carefully examining the Scriptures for ourselves. Reading what others have written will be helpful at some point, and it is to some degree necessary. Without interacting with the work of others, including those who have reached differing conclusions, one might easily overlook weaknesses in his own position. First, however, seek to reflect on the Bible alone.

Elders who agree with the permanence view may have already studied divorce and remarriage in detail. They may even have read many of the various books that have been written on this subject. Elders in this situation may not want to start completely from scratch, but may prefer instead to use this book as a guide for their group study. We would not want anyone to substitute this book for the Scriptures, but we would applaud its use as a general study guide since it represents the fruit of the type of study described in the previous paragraph.

6. *Review the applicable passages and talk through your conclusions with the men of the church.* Elders benefit greatly from the insight of spiritually minded men in the church. Provide copies of the elders' initial conclusions for the men and read them together over a period of several meetings. If this book summarizes what you have come to believe, make it available for the men to read along with anything you have written on the subject. Once they have had the chance to study your conclusions, allow time and opportunity for questions, even disagreement. Be sure that all are striving to give biblical support for the statements they make. Remind them that the goal is to discover the mind of God and for all to be in joyful submission to His directives. The elders should affirm often that their objective is only to follow the Head of the Church, Jesus Christ. Assure the men that the elders will revise the arguments and conclusions when necessary.

7. *Craft a tentative position statement.* This may either be a brief statement of core beliefs (see appendix 3) or a more lengthy position statement. If you decide to record the results of your study in a longer position paper, be sure to include both the biblical arguments for the view along with the most important practical implications that would result in the life of the church. If you choose to write (or adopt) a shorter statement (such as the one we have provided in appendix 3), you might consider making this book available as a foundation for your conclusions.

8. **Encourage all members to read and respond to the position within a clearly established time frame.** This will provide the elders with another layer of insight. Perhaps there were men in the church who were not able to participate in the study. The women who read and respond will certainly provide a needed perspective as well. Once again, consider carefully the thoughts and questions of the members. Perhaps it would be best not to have a large group meeting where members can respond to the position publicly. Instead, encourage private meetings with the elders where there might be more freedom to share concerns and receive thorough responses to questions. For those who disagree with the position, consider their arguments and adjust your views if necessary.

9. **Seek the church's affirmation.** Eventually, the elders of the church have to conclude on their view of divorce and remarriage. On such a large issue, it is helpful to ask for the church's affirmation of the position the elders have taken. Instead of asking for a simple "yes" or "no," perhaps it would be better to have people express their view of the position on more than one level so that the elders know where the church stands.

Here's what you could do: At an appropriate meeting, pass out slips of paper that contain a brief summary of the position. Ask the members to read the summary and then check a box next to one of three sentences which best expresses their belief about the position.

☐ I have studied and prayed about this issue, and believe it is the will of God that our church adopt the permanence view in doctrine and practice.

☐ I do not know the will of God in this matter, but joyfully submit to the elders' leadership concerning this particular decision.

☐ I have studied and prayed about it, and I do not believe the permanence view accurately reflects the will of God with respect to divorce and remarriage. Therefore I do not believe it is the will of God that our church adopt this position in doctrine and practice.

The elders should make it clear that they desire to meet promptly with any who checked the last statement. Since these affirmation sheets are anonymous, it would be the dissenting member's responsibility to contact the elders to set up that appointment within a short time frame (one week?).

Soon after seeking a final affirmation from the church, the elders should communicate to the church publicly and in writing (perhaps an email or letter) how the members responded. If there were numerous objectors, perhaps further teaching will be necessary before the position can be affirmed. If the affirmation procedure reveals a level of consensus that is acceptable to the elders (or is required by a constitution) then inform the church of the adoption of the position statement by the church.

If several check the last box and talk with the elders further, consider carefully what God may be saying to the church. It may be that the church should be informed that its former view will remain in place as a church policy until further discussion has taken place. This failure to settle on one clear position may mean that the elders will have to act according to their conscience, however, even if the official position of the church is different than their view, until a future attempt to unify on the issue. This admittedly puts the church in a difficult situation, yet the church does not have the freedom to avoid having a position.

10. *Begin functioning as a church according to the position.* If the permanence view is adopted, the next step is to implement it in the life of the church. Churches that honor God function according to the truth (1 Tim. 3:15), even if their actions are misunderstood and unpopular with those outside. Also, periodically teach your church about your position. Newer members will need to be instructed in the position, and long-term members will appreciate the review.

If your church does accept the permanence view, you may wish to adopt a summary statement as your official position statement.

We have included a brief position statement for this purpose in appendix 3. If your church never approves of this view, or if movement in that direction seems painfully slow, you can still lead the church to champion a high view of marriage. Continue to press patiently toward this, and do not feel defeated if full agreement seems unlikely.

Appendix 3
A Brief Church Policy Statement on Divorce and Remarriage

Because drafting a policy statement on divorce and remarriage would necessarily be a detailed and lengthy process, we encourage churches who are in agreement with the permanence view to adopt or modify the following simple statement:

> **Our view of the Bible's teaching on marriage, divorce, and remarriage is summarized in three assertions:**
>
> **1. The one-flesh union created in marriage is permanent until death.**
>
> **2. Initiating a divorce is never lawful.**
>
> **3. Remarrying after divorce is an act of adultery if a former spouse is living.**
>
> **Biblical arguments for these statements, and the practical applications that follow, are helpfully summarized in the book, *Divorce and Remarriage: A Permanence View*, by Daryl Wingerd, Jim Elliff, Jim Chrisman, and Steve Burchett. Our church is in substantial agreement with this book.**

The above statement is workable largely because *Divorce and Remarriage: A Permanence View* was originally written as a policy statement. Other books may be written on this view in the future which could be listed as additional resources.

CHRISTIAN COMMUNICATORS *Worldwide*

CCW is a ministry based in Parkville, Missouri, a "river-stop" town in the Northland of the greater Kansas City area. We enjoy this quaint town with its beautiful park, interesting shops and eateries, and the stately Park University which overlooks it all. The meandering Missouri River, navigated by Lewis and Clark on their expedition, runs along the south end of the town. Independence, Missouri, the starting place for the Oregon and Santa Fe trails, is not far from Parkville. We have a unique history here at "the beginning of the Westward advance." Like those who explored and settled the western regions of the United States, CCW is also on a mission—to extend the message of Christ as far as God will allow. We do that through our websites (see next page) and through the speaking ministry of our founder, Jim Elliff, and Steve Burchett. We also do this through Jim's writing ministry and that of his assistants, Daryl Wingerd, Susan Verstraete, and Steve Burchett. CCW publishes books and booklets, offered by us and by other booksellers. Tens of thousands of pieces of free literature have also been distributed, both here and overseas.

Please visit our web sites:

www.CCWtoday.org
This is our main site, with numerous articles, ministry tools, audio messages, and information about ordering our publications.

www.CCWblog.org
This blog revisits pertinent articles from all our sites on a weekly basis, and provides an opportunity for interaction with our writers.

www.BulletinInserts.org
This site provides timely and instructive bulletin inserts, handouts, and tracts. We offer free, downloadable inserts (also available in A4) for every Sunday of the year.

www.WaytoGod.org
This site contains articles and audio designed to guide interested people into a relationship with Jesus Christ. Here we also answer questions from inquirers.